*Pocket Guide to*

# Technical Writing

Canadian Edition

**William Sanborn Pfeiffer**
*Ramapo College of New Jersey*

**J. Boogerd**
*Algonquin College*

Toronto

**National Library of Canada Cataloguing in Publication**

Pfeiffer, William S.
        Pocket guide to technical writing / William S. Pfeiffer, J.
Boogerd. – Canadian ed.


Includes index.
ISBN 0-13-120685-0

1. English language–Technical English–Handbooks, manuals, etc.
2. English language–Rhetoric–Handbooks, manuals, etc.  3. Technical writing–
Handbooks, manuals, etc.  I. Boogerd,  Jan, 1949-  II. Title.

T11.P437 2004              808'.0666                    C2003-903466-6

ISBN 0-13-120685-0

Vice President, Editorial Director: Michael J. Young
Executive Editor: Dave Ward
Marketing Manager: Toivo Pajo
Developmental Editor: Paula Druzga
Production Editor: Judith Scott
Copy Editor: Jim Leahy
Production Manager: Patricia Ciardullo
Page Layout: Christine Velakis
Art Director: Mary Opper
Cover Design: Michelle Bellemare
Cover Image: Getty Images

19 20 21 CP 15 14 13

Printed and bound in Canada

This book first is dedicated to the memory of my parents, Hal and Jean Pfeiffer, who wrote with honesty, brevity, and style. It is also dedicated to my children, Zachary and Katie, who are learning to do the same.

*—William S. Pfeiffer*

# Preface

*T*his little book is a basic how-to manual that will help you to document information when you are on the job. It does not pretend to provide you with all there is to know about writing in a work environment. There are other, longer books which serve that purpose.

The book provides you with straightforward answers to the questions that will come up when you need to document information. The principles on which the answers are based form the foundation of every text and every course intended to teach technical writing. For that reason this book will be useful to you at school as well as at work.

In addition to its usefulness as a reference guide in the workplace, this book is well suited for technical writing courses when only a basic text is needed and for classes in scientific or technical fields when a supplement is required for the text.

## ORGANIZATION OF TEXT

The *Pocket Guide* presents information on five main subjects, each with its own chapter or appendix:

Chapter 1    The Writing Process: Achieving Speed and Quality

Chapter 2    Structure: Achieving Order and Design

Chapter 3    Special Topics: Graphics and Oral Presentations

Appendix A:  ABC Formats and Examples

Appendix B:  Writing Handbook

Each section gives you a "jump start" on planning, drafting, or revising when you are rushed to deliver a document. The two appendices will be especially useful for immediate help with writing. Appendix A includes one-page outlines for 16 different types of documents, followed by model examples of each. Appendix B contains alphabetized answers to assist with questions about style, grammar, and usage.

## ACKNOWLEDGMENTS

Sandy Pfeiffer would like to thank the following individuals and companies for allowing him to incorporate their material into examples: Jefferson Alexander, Natalie Birnbaum, David Cox, Jeffrey Daxon, Rob Duggan, Fugro-McClelland, Inc., Chuck Keller, Becky Kelly, Steven Knapp, Law Companies Group, Alan Mitchell, Jeff Orr, Chris Owen, Ken Rainey, Sam Randell, Hattie Schumaker, Herb Smith, and James Stephens.

He also thanks his family—Evelyn, Zach, and Katie—for their ever-present support during this project and for their outstanding suggestions for improving the book.

## ABOUT THE AUTHORS

Sandy Pfeiffer has spent a career in technical and professional communicaton. With a Ph.D. in English, he is currently provost and vice president for academic affairs at Ramapo College of New Jersey, a state-supported institution. In July 2003 he retired as vice president for academic affairs at Southern Polytechnic State University (SPSU) in Marietta, Georgia, where he was appointed professor emeritus. At SPSU Pfeiffer helped develop B.S. and M.S. degrees in Technical and Professional Communication, as well as a B.A. in International Technical Communication. Since 1979, he has also taught communication seminars in the U.S. and abroad.

Besides the *Pocket Guide*, Pfeiffer has written *Technical Writing: A Practical Approach*, now in its 5th edition (Prentice Hall, 2003). The book is used in colleges and universities around the country. He also wrote *Proposal Writing: The Art of Friendly Persuasion* (Merrill, 1989); co-authored, with Chuck Keller, *Proposal Writing: The Act of Friendly and Winning Persuasion* (Prentice Hall, 2000); and wrote *Pocket Guide to Public Speaking* (Prentice Hall, 2002).

Since 1979, Pfeiffer has taught communication seminars to business, industry, and government groups in the United States and overseas. Sample seminar topics include Report Writing, Proposals, Oral Presentations, Effective Meetings, and Technical Editing.

Mr. J. Boogerd is currently the chair of the Architecture/Civil/GIS/Technical Writer Department in the School of Advanced Technology at Algonquin College. The program group that comprises the department also includes English, Mathematics, General Education, and Biotechnology. Prior to accepting his current position Mr. Boogerd spent 25 years as a professor and coordinator in the English Department. In addition to his duties at Algonquin College, he has worked, on a contract basis, as a technical writer. His most recent contract was with Sharing Technologies sa.

# Brief Contents

# Contents

## Appendix A:
### *ABC Formats and Examples* 73

# 1 The Writing Process: Achieving Speed and Quality

*A*ll writers want to write quickly and well. If there were magic pills to create good writing on demand, they would outsell aspirin. Although we have no prose-producing pills, we do have simple techniques for dramatically increasing the speed and quality of your on-the-job writing. This chapter presents techniques to improve the writing process.

The "writing process" can be defined as the steps you follow to complete a successful writing project. Process is indeed the key to good writing because it separates activity into manageable stages, each of which includes specific goals. To introduce you to the writing process, this chapter has three main sections:

- **Definition of Technical Writing**—giving basic information about purpose, writers, and readers in technical writing
- **Nine Steps to Better Writing**—explaining the main steps that help you plan, draft, and revise
- **Writing in Groups**—providing five guidelines for collaborative writing projects

This chapter gives most attention to the planning process. In fact, seven of the "Nine Steps to Better Writing" take place before you even begin a first draft. To assist you in the crucial planning process, at the end of the book you will find a Planning Form to use in preparing your strategy for completing each document.

## DEFINITION OF TECHNICAL WRITING

At some point in our lives, we all do three main types of writing: academic, personal, and technical (see Figure 1–1 on the following page). Yet for most mortals, only technical writing remains the type that will determine our professional success.

| Type | Purpose | Audience | Example |
|------|---------|----------|---------|
| Academic | Display knowledge | Teachers or colleagues | Research paper |
| Personal | Enlighten, entertain | Yourself or friends | Journal, letters |
| Technical | Get something done | Supervisors, subordinates, or customers | Reports |

**FIGURE 1–1**
Three types of writing

The term *technical writing* includes all written communication done on the job. It originally referred only to writing done in fields of technology, engineering, and science, but it has come to mean writing done in *all* professions and organizations (see Figure 1–2 on the next page). Technical writing can be distinguished from other prose by features related to its (1) purpose, (2) writer, and (3) readers.

## Purpose: Getting Something Done

A practical purpose underlies all on-the-job writing. With such writing you strive to get something accomplished for your organization, for a customer, or for both. Academic writing displays knowledge, and personal writing entertains or enlightens. Although technical writing may sometimes have these goals too, its main purpose is *practical*—for example, to change a policy, offer a new product, or explain a procedure.

## Writer: Conveying Your Knowledge to the Reader

As writer, you have something to teach your readers. Usually you know more about the topic than they do—that's why *you're* writing to *them*. Readers benefit from knowledge you provide and make changes accordingly—for example, responding to problems you highlight, following recommendations you put forth, and buying products you are selling. Of course, your superior knowledge about the topic can sometimes create a problem. You must avoid talking over the heads of your readers. This challenge may be the greatest one you face as a writer.

> Writer's Job #1: Write for the Reader

**Correspondence: In-House or External**
- Memos to your boss and to your subordinates
- Routine letters to customers, vendors, etc.
- "Good news" letters to customers
- "Bad news" letters to customers
- Sales letters to potential customers
- E-mail messages to co-workers or customers over a computer network

**Short Reports: In-House or External**
- Analysis of a problem
- Recommendation
- Equipment evaluation
- Progress report on project or routine periodic report
- Report on the results of laboratory or fieldwork
- Description of the results of a company trip

**Long Reports: In-House or External**
- Complex problem analysis, recommendation, or equipment evaluation
- Project report on field or laboratory work
- Feasibility study

**Other Documents**
- Proposal to boss for new product line
- Proposal to boss for change in procedures
- Proposal to customer to sell a product, service, or idea
- Proposal to funding agency for support of research project
- Abstract or summary of technical article
- Technical article or presentation
- Operation manual or other manual

**FIGURE 1–2**
Examples of technical writing

Adapted from *Technical Writing: A Practical Approach*, 3rd Canadian Edition (p. 5) by W.S. Pfeiffer and J. Boogerd, 2004. Reprinted with permission by Pearson Education Canada Inc.

# Readers: Understanding Their Diverse Needs

Your job would be simple if each document were directed to just one reader. But actual technical writing is not that easy. Instead, a document often has *many* readers, with mixed technical backgrounds and with different needs. Even when a document goes to only one person, it may be read by other people later. This varied audience affects the structure and the language you select to drive home your message.

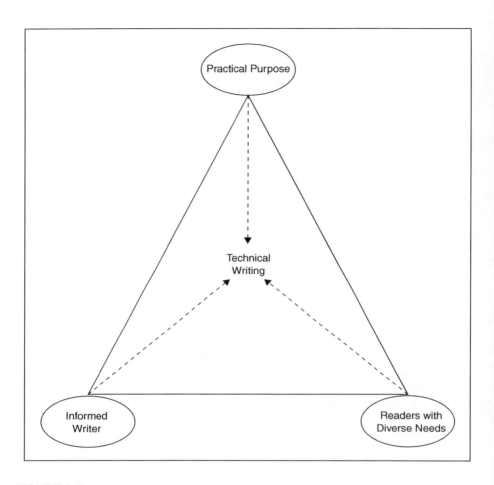

**FIGURE 1–3**
Technical writing triangle

Thus the fabric of technical writing is formed by the special combination of three elements, as shown in Figure 1–3:

1. A practical purpose
2. A writer more informed than the audience
3. Readers with diverse needs

Such writing will challenge you. The rest of this chapter shows how the challenge can be met most efficiently during the planning, drafting, and revision stages of writing.

## NINE STEPS TO BETTER WRITING

Most good writers are made, not born. They work hard at perfecting the *process* of writing. The written *product* may appear effortlessly produced, but actually it results from a disciplined approach to composition. The discipline is embodied in a nine-step plan. If you follow this plan, you will learn for yourself that there is no mystery to improving the efficiency and quality of your writing.

Of the main stages of writing—planning, drafting, and revising—the first deserves the most attention but often receives the least. An extra hour spent planning can save two or three hours of rework during the drafting and revision stages. For that reason, the first seven steps concern the planning process. Then Steps 8 and 9 offer suggestions for drafting and revising your draft.

As noted earlier on page 1, you may choose to use the Planning Form at the end of this book to help you design the best strategy for planning a document.

## *Step 1: State the Purpose of the Document*

Every document will have two levels of purpose: your purpose and the purpose you want the document to achieve. You must focus your efforts on achieving your own purpose but you will rarely state it in the document. On the other hand, you must state the purpose of the document. For example, you may be preparing a proposal for your company to outsource a potential client's IT operations. Your purpose is to win the contract. The purpose of the document would be to persuade your potential client that purchasing your IT services would result in increased efficiency and savings for them. Writing a purpose statement forces you to decide (1) exactly why you are writing, and (2) what response you want from your readers. It directs your effort and becomes the lens through which you view the entire writing project.

A purpose statement can begin with a simple phrase such as "The purpose of this report is to ̄ . . . ," or it can include more subtle phrasing. Whatever wording you choose, strive to write a passage that clearly sets forth your intentions.

### Purpose Statements

**Example 1:** This report presents the findings of our fieldwork at Trinity Dam, along with our recommendation that the spillway be replaced.

**Example 2:** The purpose of this report is to compare and contrast two computer systems being considered for Petrocan. The report draws conclusions about the system best suited for Petrocan's long-term needs.

Note that a purpose statement only indicates why you are writing. It does not present summary points such as conclusions or recommendations. It gives direction, not results, and intends only to get you started in the writing process.

## Step 2: Consider the Obstacles Your Readers Face

In an ideal world, readers would eagerly await your documents and give them their undivided attention. That ideal rarely exists. In fact, you're better off making the following assumptions about the audience members.

### They Are Always Interrupted

Meetings, phone calls, e-mail, lunch, and even business trips may interrupt them as they attempt to read your document.

### They Are Impatient

They want you to deliver the goods quickly and clearly. While they read, they are thinking, "What's the point?" or "So what?" or "What does this have to do with me?" This impatience may mean they will not, or cannot, read the document from beginning to end.

### They Have a Different Background Than You Do

They may not understand the terms you use. Thus they'll feel insulted—or just plain lost—if you speak in language they cannot understand.

To add to your challenge as a writer, most documents are viewed by different readers who may share decision-making authority and who may have different needs. The next two steps give you a way to analyze the background of diverse readers. For now, consider asking the following questions of each reader to help design a document that meets his or her needs:

1. What is the reader's technical or educational background?
2. What main question does this person need answered?
3. What main action do you want this person to take?
4. What features of this person's personality might affect his or her reading?
5. What features does this person prefer in format? Style? Organization?

These same questions are included on the Planning Form at the end of the book.

## Step 3: Determine Technical Levels of Readers

How much do your readers know about the subject? To answer this question, you can place most readers into one of the four categories that follow.

### Category 1: Managers
Managers often are removed from the hands-on details of the topic. They need brief summaries, background information, and definitions of technical terms.

### Category 2: Experts
Experts have a good understanding of the technical aspects of your topic. They need supporting technical detail, helpful tables and figures, and even appendices of supporting information.

### Category 3: Operators
Operators—such as field technicians, office workers, or members of a sales force—apply the ideas in your document to their jobs. They need (a) clear organization so that they can find sections relevant to them, (b) well-written procedures, and (c) clarity about how the document affects their jobs.

### Category 4: General Readers
General readers, also known as "laypersons," have the least amount of information on your topic and often are outside an organization—for example, citizens reading a report on the environmental impact of a factory proposed for their community. They need (a) definitions of technical terms, (b) frequent use of graphics, and (c) clear statements about how the document will affect them.

## Step 4: Determine Decision-Making Levels of Readers

Your readers also can be classified by the degree to which they make decisions based on your document. During the planning process, you can classify your readers into the following three groups.

### Decision Makers
As managers, decision makers translate your document into action. Decisions can be made by an individual or by a committee.

### Advisers
Although advisers do not make decisions themselves, they have the ear of people who do. That is, busy managers often give engineers, accountants, and others the task of analyzing technical points of a document. Final decisions may rest on recommendations that flow from this analysis.

### Receivers
Some readers are not part of the decision-making process. Instead, they receive information in the document and make adjustments in their jobs accordingly.

Figure 1–4 includes technical levels on the vertical axis and decision-making levels on the horizontal axis. It shows 12 basic categories of readers. Generally, the more categories that apply to any given writing project, the more challenging is your job in meeting the needs of a varied audience. Figure 1–4 is also part of the Planning Form included at the end of the book.

A fictional case study will demonstrate how a typical writing project easily can involve half the audience categories shown in the Figure 1–4 matrix. As the architect for a college, Megan Neeley is developing a proposal for a new entrance for the school where she works. The proposed project will include a massive stone arch, widened roadway, new traffic light, renovated bell tower, and expanded landscaping. The main goals are to enhance the appearance of the part of the college most seen by the public, improve safety and convenience for students and employees entering campus, and add enrollment by improving the visibility of the school.

In her proposal, Megan should consider the needs of the following six categories represented in Figure 1–4:

1. Decision Maker/Manager: the president of the college, who will make the decision for the college and whose main background and experience are in management
2. Decision Maker/General Reader: the mayor of the town, who will make the decision for the city and is a storekeeper-turned-politician

| Technical Level | Decision-Making Level | | |
|---|---|---|---|
| | Decision Makers | Advisers | Receivers |
| Managers | | | |
| Experts | | | |
| Operators | | | |
| General Readers | | | |

**FIGURE 1–4**
Reader matrix

Adapted from *Technical Writing: A Practical Approach,* 3rd Canadian Edition (p. 14) by W.S. Pfeiffer and J. Boogerd, 2004. Reprinted with permission by Pearson Education Canada Inc.

3. Adviser/Expert: the chief accountant at the college, who will advise the president about the proposal and is an expert in matters of finance
4. Advisers/Operators: the two traffic coordinators of the town, who will advise the mayor about the road and stop light proposals and who work every day on the town's traffic problems
5. Receivers/Managers: the four academic deans of the college, who will inform faculty about the proposal but who themselves are not part of the decision-making process
6. Receiver/General Reader: the editor of the college's student newspaper, who will write an article on the proposal for the paper but will not take part in the decision-making process

Note that in a different situation, the individuals listed above would change decision-making roles. Indeed, the purpose of this case study is to demonstrate that information about readers must be based on facts of the particular context in which you are writing.

## Step 5: Find Out What Decision Makers Want

Knowing the technical and decision-making levels of your readers is a good first step. Next, you need to focus on the needs of the most important readers—those who make decisions. Three suggestions follow.

### Write Down What You Know about Decision Makers
Specifically, try to get answers to the questions listed previously in Step 2 (and also included on the Planning Form at the end of the book).

### Talk with Colleagues Who Have Written to the Same Readers
Someone else in your organization may know the needs of the decision makers for your document. Ask around the office to see if your colleagues can help you answer the six preceding questions.

### Remember That All Readers Prefer Simplicity
When you just aren't able to find out much about the decision makers, remember one essential point about all readers: They prefer documents to be as short and simple as possible. The popular KISS principle is the best rule to follow:

---

Keep It Short and Simple!

---

## *Step 6: Collect and Document Information Carefully*

Whether you gather information yourself or get it from other sources, be careful during the research phase of the planning process. First, your reader may want to know exactly how you developed supporting data. Second, your professional reputation—and even your job—may be at risk if you err in the way you handle borrowed information. Some suggestions follow.

### Record Notes Carefully

Basic writing courses often stress the importance of taking careful notes on material borrowed from books, magazines, newspapers, interviews, or the Internet. Yet this research step is just as important—if not more important—in technical writing that you produce in college and in your career. Only by preventing errors at the earliest stages of the writing process can you ensure that a final document will have used borrowed information correctly.

Start by writing a bibliography card for each source you use. Take special care in recording information with absolute accuracy because you will use information on the card—not the source itself—when you construct your final bibliography for the paper. The second type of card is the note card. Each one contains quotations, paraphrases, or summaries based on a particular source. Figure 1–5 on the following page includes a sample bibliography card and three note cards, all based on the same passage of borrowed material. Observe the following distinctions in the three types of note cards:

1. **Quotation** cards include the exact wording of the original passage. Requiring much time to write and much space on a card, they are useful only when you're convinced the precise words of the original will be needed in your paper.
2. **Paraphrase** cards may use a few keywords from the original but require words and sentence structures that are mostly your own. They are especially useful when you want to reflect the train of ideas in the source without getting bogged down in direct quotations.
3. **Summary** cards reduce a good deal of borrowed information to a few of your own sentences. Although they may mix summary with some direct quotations—clearly indicated with quotation marks—generally summary cards use your own words to distill a large amount of text from the source.

If in the past you have used regular notebooks instead of note cards to record your research, you will be pleasantly surprised at the new flexibility provided by cards. For example, you can sort cards into topics with ease once you have written an outline (see the next step on writing an outline). Also, you can more conveniently carry them with you in a pocket or bag when you are conducting research at varied locations. Cards provide a simple, yet powerful, research strategy.

GALILEO
Academic Search Premier

Henry, E., and C. McGrath. 2000.
    Coast to coast on four fill-ups. Kiplinger's Personal
    Finance Magazine, 54.8 (August). 160+.

Mentions the Insight cult and "fudoxeia nervosa."

---

QUOTATION CARD                                    Henry + McGrath

"Although the car [Insight] will never lead the pack at
Indy, you won't fear for your life getting on the highway....
But note this: The Insight's 165.5 kilo payload capacity
means a couple of hefty passengers can overload [sic]
the car. Honda says that wouldn't damage the vehicle
but would impede performance and mileage."

---

PARAPHRASE CARD                                   Henry + McGrath

The Insight won't win any races, but it will get you safely
on the highway. Its load weight (165.5 kilos) is poor,
however. Honda says that it wouldn't damage the car
to overload it, but that performance and mileage would
suffer.

---

SUMMARY CARD                                      Henry + McGrath

The Insight has modest power but can't carry much
weight.

**FIGURE 1–5**
Research cards

Adapted from *Technical Writing: A Practical Approach*, 3rd Canadian Edition (pp. 471–473) by
W.S. Pfeiffer and J. Boogerd, 2004. Reprinted with permission by Pearson Education Canada Inc.

## Transfer Information Carefully

Most errors in documentation result from sloppy work—not from intentional cheating. But whether an error in using borrowed information is unintentional or intentional, it is *plagiarism*—that is, the parading of someone else's ideas, words, or graphics as your own. Unless information is considered "common knowledge"—namely, information generally available from many basic sources in the field—its use should include a citation to the source. In college, plagiarism can result in failing a paper or course or even being removed from school. In a career, it can result in embarrassment at best, or lawsuits and job loss at worst. So it's worth taking some time at the notetaking stage to consider ways to avoid the problem. Here are a few pointers:

- Avoid changing the meaning of a quotation if you choose to replace some words with *ellipses* (series of spaced periods—see Quotation Card example in Figure 1–5). Although ellipses can prove helpful in removing words that are not essential to your purpose, their inclusion must not alter the meaning or context of the original.
- Circle quotation marks on cards and on early drafts. Using this technique, you can easily identify material taken directly from a source. In other words, you want to make sure you don't make the error of assuming a direct quotation is one of your own paraphrases.
- Look away from your source for a few moments before you write a paraphrase or summary card. In this way you will be much more likely to use your own words and sentence structure. Then after you have written the paraphrase or summary, compare your writing to the original to be sure you have not too closely paralleled the words or structure of the original.

## Use the Right Citation System

In citations of borrowed information in the text, colleges and professional associations now favour simple systems that get the job done without fanfare. In most cases, borrowed information is identified with short parenthetical notations that occur within the text after the borrowed information (as opposed to footnotes). The references may include the author's last name, possibly the year of publication, and a page reference. Such references should follow any borrowed information—whether quotation, paraphrase, or summary—that is not considered common knowledge. For example, if you were paraphrasing some of the material in this chapter, your reference might look something like the following:

> The author indicates that writers are required to include a parenthetical reference to all borrowed information unless the information is understood to be "common knowledge" (Pfeiffer/Boogerd, 2004, 12).

Besides the parenthetical references, documentation systems usually include a list of all references cited at the end of the document. Systems may

**Book with two or more authors:** Note that the second author's name is given in normal order, with a comma between the two authors' names.

Andrews, T. S., and L. Kelly. 1965a. *Geography of central Oregon,* 4th ed. New York: Jones and Caliber Press.

**Book by same authors:** Note that the blank line indicates another source by same authors. The "b" is used because the same authors published two cited books in the same year. Also, the state abbreviation is used for clarity, since Hiram is a small town.

_____. 1965b. *Geography today.* Hiram, OH: Pixie Publishers.

**Journal article:** Note that there are no spaces between the first page number of this journal article and the colon that follows the volume number. Also, there is only a space, but no punctuation, between the journal title and the volume number.

Cranberg, E. V. 1986. Fossils are fun: The life of a geologist in the 1980s. *Geology Issues* 34:233–344.

**Article in collection:** This entry is for an article that appears in a collection, with a general editor. Note the comma and "ed." (for "edited by") after the collection title. This same format would be used in other cases where you were referring to a piece from a collection, such as a paper in a conference proceeding.

Fandell, C. N., L. Guest, H. M. Smith, and Z. H. Taylor. 1976. Achieving purity in your sampling techniques. In *Geotechnical Engineering Practices,* ed. J. Schwartz, 23–67. Cleveland: Hapsburg Press.

**Interview:** Refer to yourself in the third person as the "author."

Iris, J. G. 1988. Resident of Summer Hills Subdivision. Interview with the author at site of toxic-waste dump, 23 March.

**Newspaper article:** This reference includes the day, section, and page number of the article. If no author had been listed, the entry would have begun with the article title.

Mongo, G. P. 1989. Sinkhole psychology: The ground is falling, Chicken Little. *Dayton Gazette,* 12 July, sec. D, 5.

**Article from popular magazine:** This reference is handled like a journal article except that the date of the particular issue is also included, after the volume number. Note that there is no extra spacing around the parentheses.

Runyon, D. G., and L. P. Moss. 1967. Sinkholes are coming to your area soon. *Timely News* 123 (15 July):65–66.

**Information from personal e-mail message:** This entry concerning a personal e-mail message contains information on both sender and receiver, as well as the date and subject of the message.

Jankowski, S. X. (sjan@spdu.edu). Nature of the Mahikari movement. Personal e-mail to Matthew B. Knob (mknob@aol.com). 22 Dec. 1999.

**CD-ROM citation:** Reference to a CD-ROM does not require inclusion of the date you consulted the source.

Jasic, H. D. (1972). Japanese religions today [CD-ROM]. Available: USD Quest File Ondisc Item QF 54/4.

**FIGURE 1–6 (pp. 13–14)**
Sample list of references
Source: *Technical Writing: A Practical Approach,* 3rd Canadian Edition (pp. 13–14) by W.S. Pfeiffer and J. Boogerd, 2004. Reprinted with permission by Pearson Educaton Canada Inc.

---

**Database and Web citations:** Note that Web citations must include the date that the information was found.

Traeger, C. (n.d.) The will of the Prius. *Carlist.com*. Retrieved 10 August 2001 from the World Wide Web: *http://www.carlist.com/newcars/2001/toyotaprius.html*

Einstein, P. (1999, October 29). The benefits of Insight. *Professional Engineering*, 12.19, 23. Retrieved August 3, 2001 from GALILEO, All databases, ProQuest: *http://www.galileo.peachnet.edu*

Glynn, M. (2001, January 19). Automakers will offer "2 for the price of 1": Many major manufacturers are hoping gas-electric hybrids can power future sales. *Seattle Times*, F1. Retrieved August 4, 2001 from GALILEO, All databases, ProQuest: *http://www.galileo.peachnet.edu*

---

**FIGURE 1–6** *(continued)*

vary considerably, especially in the style of individual entries on lists of works. Thus you should use the system most acceptable to your audience or most appropriate in your professional context. Some organizations that have developed their own systems include the Modern Language Association (MLA) and American Psychological Association (APA). Another common source is the *Chicago Manual of Style*. All of the above recommend some form of parenthetical documentation and some type of list of references at the end of the document. Figure 1–6 shows one approach to a list that closely resembles systems mentioned above. You may want to use it if you are not using another system.

## Step 7: Write an Outline

Completing an outline is the single best way to write both quickly and well. This section answers three main questions: (1) Why is an outline so important? (2) What should it look like? and (3) What steps should you use in writing it?

First, why is an outline so important? Here are the main reasons.

■ **Organization:** It forces you to grapple with matters of organization at a time when it is easy to change the structure of the document—that is, before you have committed words to draft. As you add and delete ideas on the page and shift points from main to secondary topics, you are thinking about the best way to satisfy the readers' needs.

■ **Visualization:** It shows you—visually—whether you have enough supporting information. For example, if your outline includes only one subheading for a topic, you know that you need either to do more research or to delete the topic.

■ **Review:** It speeds up the review process when your documents must be approved by someone else in your organization. It is much easier to make changes at this stage than later, when you have invested time in the draft. Indeed, reviewers who "sign off" on your outline are much less likely to request major changes later.

Second, what should an outline look like? You may remember a teacher requiring you to submit a perfectly neat outline with ideal format. Such an outline is never the first version, for we just don't think that neatly. Instead, each outline will (1) start as points spread over a page without any recognizable hierarchy, (2) evolve to a recognizable list of main and supporting points, and (3) change shape during the drafting process as you adjust points of emphasis. Outlining is messy business because it reflects the thinking you do *before* you write.

Third, what steps should you use in writing an outline? Follow the sequence below. Figure 1–7 on the next page shows the result of the first two steps. Figure 1–8 on page 18 shows a later outline resulting from the third step.

## Record Random Ideas Quickly
This "nonlinear" (translate—messy) process involves the free association of ideas. To stay on track, write your purpose statement at the top of the page. Then scribble down as many points as possible that relate to the topic.

## Show Relationships
Surveying your page of ideas, locate the three or four main points that indicate the direction your document will take. Circle them. Then draw lines to connect these main points to their many supporting points, as shown in Figure 1–7.

## Draft a Final Outline
Your messy outline now must be cleaned up to make it useful to you as you write. You can either use the traditional format with Roman numerals, etc. (see Figure 1–8), or you can simply use dashes and indenting to indicate outline levels. Whatever format you employ, the final outline should reflect three main features:

■ **Depth:** Be sure the entire outline has enough support to develop the draft.
■ **Balance:** Include adequate detail for all of your main points. When you subdivide a point, have at least two breakdowns—any object divided has at least two parts.
■ **Parallel form:** Give points in the same grouping the same grammatical form, both to make the outline easier to read and to ease the transition later to parallel text in the first draft. In fact, consider keeping the entire outline consistent in form—for example, by using either full sentences or fragments for your points. Fragments are preferable because they take up less space and don't lock you into sentences too early.

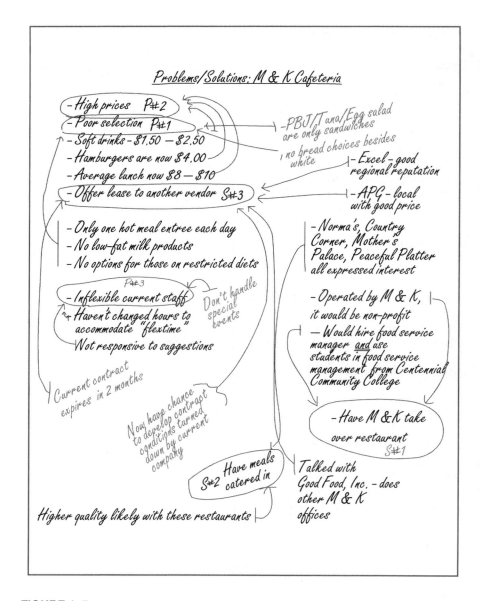

**FIGURE 1–7**

The outlining process: Early stage

Source: *Technical Writing: A Practical Approach,* 3rd Canadian Edition (p. 19) by W.S. Pfeiffer and J. Boogerd, 2004. Reprinted with permission by Pearson Education Canada Inc.

**PROBLEMS AND SOLUTIONS: CURRENT CAFETERIA IN BUILDING**

I. Problem #1: Poor selection
  A. Only one hot meal entree each day
  B. Only three sandwiches—PBJ, egg salad, and tuna
  C. Only one bread—white
  D. No low-fat milk products (milk, yogurt, LF cheeses, etc.)
  E. No options for those with restricted diets
II. Problem #2: High prices
  A. Soft drinks from $1.50 to $2.50 each
  B. Hamburgers now $4.00
  C. Average lunch now $8–$10
III. Problem #3: Inflexible staff
  A. Unwilling to change hours to meet M & K's flexible work schedule
  B. Have not acted on suggestions
  C. Not willing to cater special events in building
IV. Solution #1: End lease and make food service a M & K department
  A. Hire food service manager
  B. Use students enrolled in food service management program at Centennial Community College
  C. Operate as non-profit operation—just cover expenses
V. Solution #2: Hire outside restaurant to cater meals into building
  A. Higher quality likely
  B. Initial interest by four nearby restaurants
    1. Norma's
    2. Country Corner
    3. Mother's Palace
    4. Peaceful Platter
VI. Solution #3: Continue leasing space but change companies
  A. Initial interest by three vendors
    1. Excel—good regional reputation for quality
    2. APG—close by and local, with best price
    3. Good Food, Inc.—used by two other M & K offices with good results
  B. Current contract over in two months
  C. Chance to develop contract not acceptable to current company

**FIGURE 1–8**

The outlining process: Later stage

*Source: Technical Writing: A Practical Approach,* 3rd Canadian Edition (p. 22) by W. S. Pfeiffer, and J. Boogerd, 2004, Reprinted with permission by Pearson Education Canada Inc.

With outline in hand, you are ready to begin the second part of the three-part writing process—drafting.

## Step 8: Write Your First Draft Quickly

The first draft offers you another chance to speed up the writing process. Unfortunately, this is when many writers encounter "writer's block" and slow down. What follow are suggestions for capturing time often wasted at this stage. Of course, the most important suggestion was covered in the previous step—*always* enter the drafting stage with a complete outline in hand.

### Schedule Blocks of Drafting Time

Writing requires concentration. Close your door if you have one, head to an empty office, or write at home—just do whatever you must to keep from being interrupted for at least 30 to 60 minutes. By giving writing a priority, you will finish drafts in record time. However, if you allow every other activity to upset your drafting schedule, writing even a simple document will consume your day.

### Don't Stop to Edit

Editing uses a different part of your brain than drafting does. When you stop to correct grammar or spelling errors, you derail the drafting effort. With each interruption it becomes harder and harder to regain the concentration needed to write the draft. Save editing for later.

### Begin with the Easiest Section

A well-structured outline gives you the luxury of starting with almost any part of the document. Skip around if doing so allows you to write the draft more quickly.

### Write Summaries Last

Summary sections—like the executive summary for a formal report—usually get written last. They require the kind of thoughtful overviews and careful wording that you can write best after you've seen where the entire document is going. Of course, you can write a summary at any time if you have a good outline. It's just that you will write the *best* one when you have the chance to view a completed draft of the rest of the document.

Your goal is to get words on paper quickly. Following the suggestions above will save you hours each week, days each year, and weeks over a career. The ideas are simple, but they work.

## Step 9: Revise in Stages

During revision, you must attend to matters of content, style, grammar, and mechanics. The trick to solving a variety of editing problems is to adopt a "divide-and-conquer" approach. Review the draft several times, correcting a different set of problems on each run-through. This effort to focus your attention on specific problems yields the best results. Four stages of revision follow.

## Adjust and Reorganize Content

This task could be considered either the first stage of revision or the last stage of drafting. Here you expand sections that need more development, shorten some sections, and change the location of some passages.

## Edit for Style

*Style* refers to changes that make your writing smoother, more readable, and more interesting. Here are options to consider:

- Shorten sentences
- Improve clarity—for example, by adding transitional words and by re-wording passages to show the logical flow of ideas
- Change passive-voice sentences to active
- Define technical terms
- Add headings, lists, and graphics
- Replace longer words with synonyms that are shorter or easier to understand

## Edit for Grammar

Grammar haunts all of us. Your head may be filled with dozens of half-remembered rules and terms from school days—comma splices, sentence fragments, subject–verb agreement, and dangling participles, to name just a few. You want to follow the rules, but you're no English teacher and certainly don't have time to become one. The answer to this dilemma is twofold:

- First, use your own knowledge or the editorial advice of another to determine the most common grammatical errors in your writing. Focus mainly on this short list—*not* on all grammatical errors—when you edit.
- Second, use Appendix B of this book as an editing resource while you write.

## Edit for Mechanics

Examples of mechanical errors include the following:

- Omitted words or phrases
- Misspelled words
- Inconsistent margins
- Wrong paging
- Nonparallel format in headings or subheadings

Word processing has made such errors less common and easier to correct. But technology also has lulled us into a false sense of security. You need to remain vigilant in spotting the potentially embarrassing errors that may have worked their way into your draft.

In summary, these nine steps comprise a strategy for writing every kind of on-the-job document. They require you to apply the same degree of organization to writing that you apply to other parts of your job. After all, how much of your average day do you spend writing? 20 percent? 30 percent? 50 percent? Using a disciplined method will help you use that time more efficiently, while producing better work.

Figure 1–9 compresses the nine guidelines in this chapter into a writing checklist to use for any document.

---

**Directions:** The following checklist addresses the nine guidelines in this chapter. The only change here is that the guidelines are written as questions for you to consider as you are writing.

**PLANNING**
1. Have you written a brief purpose statement?          _____
2. Have you considered the obstacles your readers face?          _____
3. Do you know the technical levels of your readers?          _____
4. Do you know the decision-making levels of your readers?          _____
5. Do you know exactly what decision makers want?          _____
6. Have you collected and documented information carefully?          _____
7. Have you written an outline?          _____

**DRAFTING**
8. Have you written the first draft quickly?          _____

**REVISING**
9. Have you revised in stages?          _____

---

**FIGURE 1–9**
Writing checklist

## *WRITING IN GROUPS*

Group writing is common in today's organizations, which emphasize teamwork at all levels and in all activities. For example, a successful proposal or technical manual may result from the combined effort of technical specialists, marketing experts, graphic artists, writers, editors, and word processors. At its best, group writing benefits from the collective experience and specialties of all participants. This section describes five pointers for keeping a collaborative writing project on track:

1. Get to know your group
2. Set clear goals and ground rules
3. Use brainstorming techniques
4. Agree on a revision process
5. Use computers to communicate

## Guideline 1: Get to Know Your Group

If you're used to being a "lone ranger"—that is, a solitary writer—you have some adjustments to make in reaching consensus during a group project. The best way to open the channels of communication is to learn as much as possible about your colleagues. Here are two techniques for doing so:

1. Spend time talking to group members before the project begins, establishing a personal relationship, or
2. Use the first session for informal chatting, before you get down to business.

The point is this: The success of your group project may depend as much on having a good working relationship as it does on the technical specialties each member brings to the table.

## Guideline 2: Set Clear Goals and Ground Rules

All groups should set goals and establish operating rules. Specifically, the following questions must be answered either before or during the first meeting:

- What is the main objective?
- How will tasks be distributed?
- How will conflicts be resolved?
- What's the schedule for the work?

## Guideline 3: Use Brainstorming Techniques

The most common error in group work is getting too critical too quickly. Just as an individual writer needs the chance to spill ideas onto paper during the outline stage, members of a group also need a chance to share ideas openly without concern for criticism. That opportunity for a nonjudgmental pooling of ideas—or "brainstorming"—comes at the beginning of the group's work. Here's one strategy for brainstorming:

1. Ask the group recorder to take down ideas as quickly as possible.
2. Write ideas on large pieces of paper affixed to the walls in a room.
3. Use ideas written on the wall sheets to suggest additional ideas.
4. Distribute results of the exercise to group members after the meeting.
5. Meet again to choose ideas of most use in the project.

## Guideline 4: Agree on a Revision Process

Group drafting and editing can be difficult. Some people used to writing in solitude find it hard to reach consensus on matters of style. Follow these suggestions for keeping the collaborative process on track:

1. Avoid making changes for the sake of one individual's preference.
2. Search for areas of agreement among members, not areas of disagreement.
3. Make only those style and grammar changes that can be supported by rules of style, grammar, and word use (see Appendix B).
4. Ask the group's all-around best stylist to complete a final edit.

Your goal should be a document that sounds as much as possible as if it were written by one person.

## Guideline 5: Use Computers to Communicate

Whether group members are in the same building or spread out across the world, they can benefit from using computers to communicate about the project. This technology, though changing as this book is written falls into two general categories:

- **Asynchronous:** Such software permits members to post messages to each other and to alter a document, though not at the same time that other group members are making contributions.
- **Synchronous:** Software of this type allows group members to carry on simultaneous computer "conversations" about a document in real time. With several windows on their screens, they can place messages on the screen at the same time they edit a document that appears on the screen of all participants involved in the computer conversation.

Computer conversations can go well beyond e-mail. Perhaps the greatest advantage they lend to group work is the openness encouraged by such on-line discussions. When coordinated with face-to-face sessions, such computer meetings produce results.

# 2 Structure: Achieving Order and Design

*G*ood structure will impress your readers. They respond well to inviting, easy-to-read documents. The purpose of this chapter is to help you apply simple rules about structure to everything you write.

*Structure* is defined here as both the arrangement of information within the document *(organization)* and the techniques used to highlight information *(page design)*. This chapter includes guidelines on both aspects of structure. Three main sections follow:

- **Basics of Organization**—describes the main rule of technical writing and the three principles that flow from it
- **ABC Format**—outlines a three-part pattern of organization—abstract, body, conclusion—that applies to all technical documents
- **Page Design**—explains simple formatting techniques that can improve any technical document

Together, the three sections provide an "executive summary" about structure in technical writing. Refer to Appendix A, which includes ABC Format outlines and accompanying models for 16 common documents. It can serve as a starting point for your on-the-job writing projects.

## BASICS OF ORGANIZATION

As noted in Chapter 1, readers may differ greatly in technical background and decision-making authority. Yet most share four features: (1) they are interrupted while reading, (2) they are impatient to find important information, (3) they lack your knowledge of the topic, and (4) the documents they read are seen by others too. Any principles of organization must respond to this set of features, for there is one cardinal rule of all technical writing:

> Write for your reader, not for yourself.

This rule sounds sensible enough. However, following it will challenge you when you have many readers with varying needs. Sometimes it is hard to find the right approach. This section presents three guidelines to remember as you plan, draft, and revise documents for readers of mixed technical backgrounds.

## Structure Rule 1: Write Different Parts for Different Readers

The longer the document, the less likely it is that anyone will read it from beginning to end. Readers use a "speed-read" approach that includes these steps:

**Step 1:  Quick scan.** Readers scan easy-to-read sections like executive summaries, introductory summaries, introductions, tables of contents, conclusions, and recommendations. They pay special attention to beginning and ending sections, especially in documents longer than a page or two, and to illustrations.

**Step 2:  Focused search.** Readers go directly to parts of the document body that will give them what they need at the moment. To find information quickly, they search for format devices like subheadings, listings, and white space in margins to guide their reading.

**Step 3:  Short follow-ups.** Readers return to the document, when time permits, to read or reread important sections.

In other words, you can't count on readers to digest information in the same order you present it. Fortunately, you can use this fact to your advantage by writing different sections of documents for different readers. For example, the lead-off summary for a report may respond especially to the needs of managers, whereas technical sections in the body may be directed toward different groups of experts.

Writing different parts for different readers does present one hazard. If you go too far in tailoring sections for different readers, the document may become fragmented. To remedy this problem, use common threads of organization, theme, and style to help sections hang together as one piece of work. For example, each section of a long proposal could begin with a purpose statement, emphasize related selling points, use frequent headings, and include more active- than passive-voice sentences—even though the different sections were directed toward different readers.

## Structure Rule 2: Emphasize Beginnings and Endings

Most of us read fiction and essays much differently than we read technical writing. With the former, we read patiently until plot information and new knowledge come our way. With the latter, we rush to find essential information and are impatient when we don't find it quickly.

In technical writing you must accommodate impatient readers by placing important information where they want it—at the beginning and end of the document. Figure 2–1 shows how this emphasis on beginnings and endings responds to the interest level of readers. Note that interest peaks at the beginning. Here is where the reader needs you to answer the classic "so what" question:

> "So what does this document mean to me?"

As explained in the next section, the beginning part presents just an overview of important information, not details. Specifics of major interest—like detailed lists of conclusions and recommendations—come at the end.

## Structure Rule 3: Repeat Key Points

Most people will read your document selectively—not sequentially from beginning to end. This fact means that important information should be repeated, especially in longer documents.

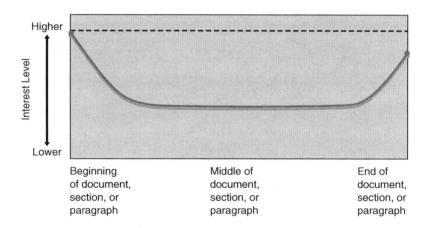

**FIGURE 2–1**
Reader interest curve
Source: *Technical Writing: A Practical Approach*, 3rd Canadian Edition (p. 53) by W.S. Pfeiffer and J. Boogerd, 2004. Reprinted with permission by Pearson Education Canada Inc.

For example, a formal report may mention a key recommendation in the cover letter, in the executive summary, and in the conclusions and recommendations section. Or a purpose statement for the report may show up, perhaps with different wording, in the cover letter, executive summary, and introduction. Needless repetition is not being advocated here. But strategic repetition does make sense if you are delivering key information to different sets of readers.

The main principle of technical writing—write for your reader, not for yourself—and the three guidelines just covered lead directly to a pattern of organization you can use in all career writing.

## ABC FORMAT

In the *Poetics*, Aristotle claimed that a literary work, to be considered "whole," must have a beginning, middle, and end. And so it is true over 2,300 years later with technical writing. Here the simple three-part structure of technical writing is labelled the ABC format (for abstract, body, and conclusion).

Figure 2–2 gives a visual representation of the ABC format; it also shows how the sections of the report in Figure 2–3 "map" on to this ABC format.

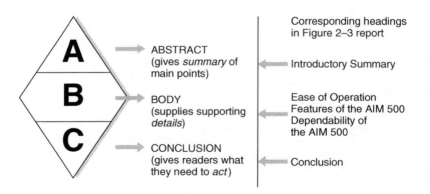

**FIGURE 2–2**
ABC format for all documents
Source:*Technical Writing: A Practical Approach,* 3rd Canadian Edition (p. 56) by W.S. Pfeiffer and J. Boogerd, 2004. Reprinted with permission by Pearson Education Canada Inc.

MEMORANDUM

DATE:      September 5, 2003
TO:        Danielle Firestein
FROM:      Barbara Ralston *BR*
SUBJECT:   Recommendation for AIM 500 Fax

**INTRODUCTORY SUMMARY**
    This memo presents my evaluation of the AIM 500 facsimile (fax) machine by Simko, Inc. The AIM 500 has served our department well for the past two years. If other departments need a fax machine, I highly recommend this model because it is easy to operate, has many useful features, and has been quite dependable.

**EASE OF OPERATION**
    The AIM 500 is so easy to operate that a novice can learn to transmit a document to another location in about two minutes. Here's the basic procedure:

1. Press the button marked TEL on the face of the fax machine. You then hear a dial tone.
2. Key in the telephone number of the person receiving the fax on the number pad on the face of the machine.
3. Lay the document face down on the tray at the back of the machine.

    At this point, just wait for the document to be transmitted—about 18 seconds per page to transmit. The fax machine will even signal the user with a beep and a message on its LCD display when the document has been transmitted. Other more advanced operations are equally simple to use and require little training. Provided with the machine are two different charts that illustrate the machine's main functions.

    The size of the AIM 500 makes it easy to set up almost anywhere in an office. The dimensions are 38 cm in width, 33 cm in length, and 12 cm in height. The narrow width, in particular, allows the machine to fit on most desks, file cabinets, or shelves.

**FEATURES OF THE AIM 500**
    The AIM 500 has many features that will be beneficial to our employees. In the two years of use in our department, the following features were found to be most helpful:

Automatic redial
Last number redial memory
LCD display

**FIGURE 2–3  (pp. 27–28)**
Short report in ABC format

---

Ralston to Firestein, 2

Preset dialling
Group dialling
Use as a phone

**Automatic Redial.** Often when sending a fax, the sender finds the receiving line busy. The redial feature will automatically redial the busy number at 30-second intervals until the busy line is reached, saving the sender considerable time.

**Last Number Redial Memory.** Occasionally there may be interference on the telephone line or some other technical problem with the transmissions. The last number memory feature allows the user to press one button to automatically trigger the machine to retry the number.

**LCD Display.** This display feature clearly shows pertinent information, such as error messages that tell a user exactly why a transmission was not completed.

**Preset Dialling.** The AIM 500 can store 16 preset numbers that can be engaged with one-touch dialing. This feature makes the unit as fast and efficient as a sophisticated telephone.

**Group Dialling.** Upon selecting two or more of the preset telephone numbers, the user can transmit a document to all of the preset numbers at once.

**Use as a Phone.** The AIM 500 can also be used as a telephone, providing the user with more flexibility and convenience.

**DEPENDABILITY OF THE AIM 500**
 Over the entire two years our department has used this machine, there have been no complaints. We always receive clear copies from the machine, and we never hear complaints about the documents we send out. This record is all the more impressive in light of the fact that we average 32 outgoing and 15 incoming transmissions a day. Obviously, we depend heavily on this machine.
 So far, the only required maintenance has been to change the paper and the dust cover.

**CONCLUSION**
 The success our department has enjoyed with the AIM 500 compels me to recommend it highly. The ease of operation, many exceptional features, and record of dependability are all good reasons to purchase additional units. If you have further questions about the AIM 500, please contact me at extension 3646.

---

**FIGURE 2–3 *(continued)***

The diamond pattern is used because it implies the following important points about the abstract, body, and conclusion sections:

■ The **abstract** provides introductory and summary information. It is represented by the narrow top of the diamond because it is brief and leads into the body.

- The **body** supplies all supporting details for the document. It is represented by the broad expansive section of the diamond because it is the longest part of a document.
- The **conclusion** gives readers what they need to act. It is represented by the narrow bottom section of the diamond because it is brief and leads away from the body section.

In this model, note that the terms *abstract, body,* and *conclusion* refer to *generalized* parts of a document, *not* to specific headings. The exact headings used to represent these sections in documents will vary, depending on the document you're writing and the organization where you work. (See Figure 2–3.) Think of the ABC format as a *general* organizational pattern. Within it you can fit the diverse sections of any document. What follow are guidelines for writing each of the sections. Remember that Appendix A gives ABC formats and models for 16 common documents.

## ABC Rule 1: The Abstract Gives the "Big Picture"

The abstract component gives readers, especially decision makers, both introductory and summary information. Specifically, it answers four questions:

1. **Purpose:** Why are you writing?
2. **Scope:** What work did you do?
3. **Results:** What main point do decision makers want to know?
4. **Contents:** What main sections follow?

If you answer these four questions at the outset, you have given readers a capsule version of the entire document and a reason to keep reading.

In a short report or letter, the abstract might be embodied in the first few sentences. It may have a heading like "introduction" or "introductory summary" (see Figure 2–3) or it may have no heading at all. In a long report, the abstract may encompass several sections, such as the letter of transmittal, executive summary, and introduction. Thus the term *abstract*—as used in this book—is a construct to help you write. It can, and often does, include several document sections that, when viewed together, make up an overview.

The two paragraphs that follow satisfy the criteria for an abstract. They are from a short in-house report.

> This report describes the results of a study that compared two laser printers being considered for bulk purchase: the CopyX 3000 and Printeze 101. We studied the marketing brochures, talked to users at several firms, and tried several models loaned to us by the manufacturers.
>
> We recommend the Printeze 101. The following report supports our recommendation with information about reliability, economy of operation, and print quality. The appendix includes technical data and testimonials from three users.

## ABC Rule 2: The Body Gives Supporting Details

The document body relates details of your work. It is especially useful to technical readers who want to see support for your conclusions or recommendations. As such, it answers these kinds of questions:

- **Background:** What led up to the project?
- **Methods:** How did you gather information?
- **Data:** What information resulted from the field, lab, or office work conducted during the study?

In some documents, the body can also include detailed conclusions and recommendations—especially if such conclusions and recommendations are the main thrust of the document. In other documents, conclusions and recommendations are a brief capstone for the document and thus are reserved for a final short section. In any case, follow four general guidelines for the document body.

### Use Lead-ins at the Beginning of Sections

Lead-ins give readers a road map for what follows. They can be as simple as a list of the subsections that follow in a section. Readers need such direction finders, in the same way they need an overview at the beginning of the whole document.

### Include Listings

Almost any series of three or more points should make you consider a listing. (See the "Lists" entries in Appendix B.) Bulleted or numbered lists are easier to read than long paragraphs of text, as long as you keep lists from becoming too long. Five to nine items are a maximum.

### Use Graphics

Graphics draw attention to important points. They are especially useful in presenting data to technical readers, most of whom expect effective graphics.

### Separate Facts from Opinions

Be clear about where opinions begin and end. Body sections usually move from facts to opinions, just like technical projects themselves. To make distinctions clear, preface your opinions with phrases like "We believe that" or "I think that."

In summary, the body sections of each document should present supporting information with clarity, with structure, and with interest.

## ABC Rule 3: The Conclusion Provides a Wrap-Up

The conclusion component varies considerably from document to document. Generally, it answers questions like the following:

- **Results:** What are your conclusions and recommendations?
- **Action:** What happens next?
- **Emphasis:** What single point would you like to leave with readers?
- **Personal note:** What can you add that will enhance your relationship with readers?

Because readers focus on beginnings and endings, you must exploit the opportunity provided by the conclusion part of the ABC format.

As with the abstract and body, the conclusion is an umbrella term for any various heading labels used at the end of documents. Possible headings are Conclusions, Recommendations, Conclusions and Recommendations, Closing, and Closing Remarks. Extremely short documents, like letters, may end with a closing paragraph that has no heading. In any case, the conclusion component of the ABC format provides the document with closure—the sense of an ending.

## PAGE DESIGN

The previous section covered organization, or the arrangement of information within a document. This section deals with the other element of structure—that is, the "look" of the document, or page design.

> **Page Design:** The collection of formatting techniques used to draw attention to your writing and engage the interest of readers. Examples include use of white space, headings, lists, and varied typefaces.

Here's one way to view page design: The ABC format forms the *deep* structure of your document, whereas page design forms the *surface* structure. Deep structure takes precedence and provides the raw material for designing pages. Yet page design can greatly influence readers. If you can capture their attention with well-designed pages, you will be more likely to engage their long-term interest in the document. This section covers three basic rules of page design.

### Design Rule 1: Use White Space Liberally

*White space* refers to spaces devoid of text or graphics. Empty space on the page acts like a magnet in drawing the reader's eye to text. It can also relieve visual monotony of printed words. Here are some suggestions for using white space effectively; Figure 2–4 shows these suggestions put to use.

Example of text
framed with white space

Example of double
columns used in
formal document

Example of letter with
ragged right margin and
extra line space between
single-spaced indented paragraphs

Example of headings
with more space above
than below them

**FIGURE 2–4**
Use of white space

Adapted from *Technical Writing: A Practical Approach* 3rd Canadian Edition (pp. 81–82) by
W.S. Pfeiffer and J. Boogerd, 2004. Reprinted with permisson by Pearson Education Canada Inc.

### Frame Text with 1" to 1 ½" Margins

You may want to use an even greater margin at the bottom of the page. If your document is bound, remember to add extra margin space on the left.

### Experiment with Double Columns

Long lines of text can tire the eyes, so you may want to try double columns in some documents. The extra space between the columns can help readers move down the page. However, the double-column look can also present problems: (1) it may look too stilted for informal documents like short letter reports, (2) its "newspaper" appearance may encourage a cursory reading, and (3) the placement of graphics becomes challenging.

### Skip Lines between Paragraphs in Single-Spaced Text

The extra line space provides visual relief in a sea of text. You should continue to indent paragraphs, however. Most readers prefer the visual break that paragraph indenting adds.

### Use Ragged Right Margins in Short Documents

The uneven edge adds visual variety needed to keep the reader's attention. Reserve a right-justified margin for some formal documents, where a book-like appearance is expected.

### Use Slightly More Space above Headings than below Them

The additional space helps to separate a heading and related text from what came before it.

## Design Rule 2: Use Headings and Subheadings Often

Headings are labels used to introduce new sections and subsections. Besides helping readers stay on track, they provide visual relief from the monotony of text and assist in finding specific information later. Following are some suggestions for producing an effective heading structure.

### Use Your Outline to Create Headings and Subheadings

A well-organized outline provides the headings and subheadings for the text. Use the following general rules for headings:

- Avoid single subheadings for a heading (anything divided has at least two parts)
- Maintain parallel grammatical form in headings of equal importance
- Try to have at least one heading on each page of text

### Use Substantive Wording

Readers prefer headings that reflect content. Use concrete language rather than abstract nouns, even if the heading ends up being longer. Thus "Surveying the Graduates" would be preferable to "Methodology," and "Background on the Bentley Dam Failure" would be preferable to "Background."

### Establish a Clear Visual Ranking of Headings

Readers should be able to identify heading levels easily as they scan a document. That is, each level should be distinctive. Figure 2–5 on the next page shows a few alternative systems for headings. There are no hard-and-fast rules for heading format. In general, keep the structure simple and neat—with a hierarchy that is clear to readers.

## *Design Rule 3: Use Lists Frequently*

As a design element, lists distinguish technical writing from other types of documents like magazine essays and fiction. Almost by definition, technical writing invites you to cluster information in lists of bulleted and numbered items. Follow the suggestions below for the most effective use of lists.

### Keep Lists Short

Experts say that the maximum length of a list should reflect the number of items people retain in their short-term memory—no more than five to nine items. (Three is the usual minimum for a list.) If you have more than nine items, create a grouped list with several major categories—almost in the form of an outline. This format gives readers a way to grasp information. For example, the many suggestions for page design in this section are grouped under four main rules.

### Use Bullets and Numbers

Bullets, or enlarged dots, work best in short lists where there is no sequence. Numbers are useful when items reflect a sequence (steps in a process) or ranking (priorities for a selection). Avoid using numbers simply because a list is long, for readers will infer sequence even if you don't intend it.

### Punctuate, Space, and Capitalize Lists Properly

An entry in Appendix B (Lists: Punctuation on page 189) presents several punctuation options for listings. The most common approach is (1) to avoid punctuation between items in a list made up of sentence fragments and (2) to capitalize the first word of each item in a list.

### Use Proper Lead-ins and Parallel Structure

Like headings, lists are preceded by lead-ins that should be complete grammatical units followed by colons. For example, "We have planned to" should be replaced by "We have planned the following activities:" Also, items in the

**FIGURE 2–5  (pp. 35–36)**
Some heading options

Adapted from *Technical Writing: A Practical Approach*, 3rd Canadian Edition (pp. 86–87) by
W.S. Pfeiffer and J. Boogerd, 2004. Reprinted with permission by Pearson Education Canada Inc.

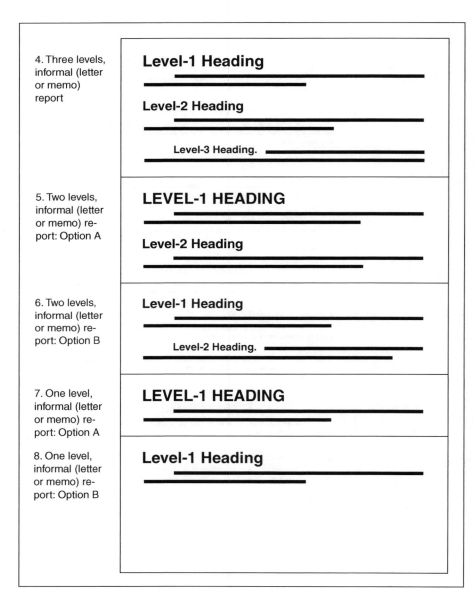

**FIGURE 2–5** *(continued)*

<u>**New Century Schoolbook**</u>
9 point
10 point
12 point
14 point
18 point
24 point

<u>**Times Roman**</u>
9 point
10 point
12 point
14 point
18 point
24 point

<u>**Helvetica**</u>
9 point
10 point
12 point
14 point
18 point
24 point

**FIGURE 2–6**
Examples of font size and types
Source: *Technical Writing: A Practical Approach*, 3rd Canadian Edition (p. 92) by W.S. Pfeiffer and J. Boogerd, 2004. Reprinted with permission by Pearson Education Canada Inc.

same list should have parallel grammatical form. (See the Lists: General Pointers entry on page 185 in Appendix B for more on parallelism.)

## *Design Rule 4: Use Fonts Effectively*

Another design option you have is font size and type. Font size generally is measured in "points" (72 points to an inch). Your computer's font-selection menu may list sizes such as 9, 10, 12, 18, and so on. As for font type, they are classified into two main groups: serif, which have "tails" at the end of letterlines, and sans serif, which do not have tails. Figure 2–6 shows three different font types in different point sizes. New Century Schoolbook and Times Roman are serif; Helvetica is sans serif.

If you are choosing the font yourself, consider criteria such as the purpose of the document, the image you want to convey, and any information you have about reader preferences. Following are additional guidelines:

1. **Use serif fonts for regular text in your documents.** The tails on letters make letters and entire words more visually interesting to the reader's eye. In this sense, they serve the same purpose as ragged-edge copy—helping your reader move smoothly through the document.
2. **Consider using another typeface—sans serif—for headings.** Headings benefit from a clean look that emphasizes the white space around letters. Sans serif type helps attract attention to these elements of organization within your text.
3. **Avoid too many font variations in the same document.** There is a fine line between interesting font variations and busy and distracting text. But there *is* a line. Your rule of thumb might be to use no more than two fonts per document, one for text and another for headings and subheadings.

This chapter has presented only the "big picture" about structure, format, and page design. As you apply the basic rules included here, refer to the document models in Appendix A to assist you in your own specific writing tasks.

# 3 Special Topics: Graphics and Oral Presentations

*T*his chapter covers two topics of special importance to you in the work-place: graphics and oral presentations (also referred to as speeches). Most of your documents will include graphics, so you need to know general guidelines for their use and specific rules for some common graphic types. As well, you often will be called upon to deliver oral presentations that explain facts or opinions to your managers or customers.

## GRAPHICS

You do not have to be an expert to understand and use graphics. However, the availability of high-tech graphics has made it important that technical professionals understand some graphics fundamentals before applying so-phisticated techniques. To emphasize these basics, this section (1) defines some common graphics terms, (2) explains the main reasons to use graphics and gives some general guidelines, and (3) lists specific guidelines for five common graphics.

### Terms in Graphics

Terminology for graphics is not uniform in the professions. That fact can lead to some confusion. For the purposes of this chapter, however, some common definitions are adopted and listed here:

- **Graphics:** This generic term refers to any nontextual portion of docu-ments or oral presentations. It can be used in two ways: (1) to designate the field (for example, "Graphics is an area in which he showed great in-terest") or (2) to name individual graphical items ("She placed three graphics in her report").
- **Illustrations, visual aids:** Used synonymously with "graphics," these terms also can refer to all nontextual parts of a document. The term *visual aids,* however, often is limited to the context of oral presentations.

- **Tables, figures:** These terms name the two subsets of graphics. *Tables* refers to illustrations that place numbers or words in columns or rows or both. *Figures* refers to all graphics other than tables. Examples include charts (pie, bar, line, flow, and organization), engineering drawings, maps, and photographs.
- **Charts, graphs:** A subset of "figures," these synonymous terms refer to a type of graphic that displays data in visual form—as with bars, pie shapes, or lines on graphs. *Chart* is the term used most often in this text.

Of course, you may see other graphics terms. For example, some technical companies use the word *plates* for figures. Be sure to know the terms your readers understand and the types of graphics they use.

## *Reasons for Using Graphics*

Before deciding whether to use a pie chart, table, or any other graphic, you need to know what graphics do for your writing. Here are four main reasons for using them.

### Reason 1: Graphics Simplify Ideas
Readers usually know less about the subject than you. Graphics can help them cut through technical details and grasp basic ideas. For example, a simple illustration of a laboratory instrument, such as a Bunsen burner, makes the description of a lab procedure much easier to understand. In a more complex example, Figure 3–1 on the next page uses a group of four different charts to convey the one main point—that a company's new Equipment Development group lags behind the company's other profit centres. A quick look at the charts tells the story of the group's difficulties much better than would several hundred words of text.

### Reason 2: Graphics Reinforce Ideas
When a point really needs emphasis, create a graphic. For example, you might draw a map to show where computer terminals will be located within a building, or use a pie chart to show how a budget will be spent, or include a drawing that indicates how to operate a VCR. In all three cases, the graphic would reinforce points made in the accompanying text.

### Reason 3: Graphics Create Interest
Graphics are "grabbers." They can be used to entice readers into the text, just as they engage readers' interest in magazines and journals. If your customers have three reports on their desks and must quickly decide which one to read first, they probably will pick up the one with an engaging picture or chart on the cover page. It may be something as simple as (1) a

**Problems in Equipment Development Group**

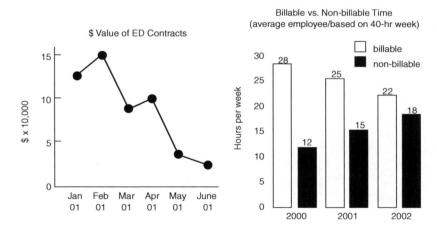

**FIGURE 3–1**
Graphics used to simplify ideas

map outline of the province, county, or city where you will be doing a project; (2) a picture of the product or service you are providing; or (3) a symbol of the purpose of your writing project. Whether on the cover or in the text, graphics attract attention.

### Reason 4: Graphics Are Universal

Some people wrongly associate the growing importance of graphics with today's reliance on television and other popular media—as if graphics pander to lower intellectual instincts. Although visual media such as television obviously rely on pictures, the fact is that graphics have been humankind's universal language since cave drawings. A picture, drawing, or chart makes an immediate emotional impact that can help or hurt your case. Advertisers know the power of images, but writers of technical documents must also merge the force of graphics with their text.

## General Guidelines

A few basic guidelines apply to all graphics. Keep these fundamentals in mind as you move from one type of illustration to another.

### Graphics Guideline 1: Refer to All Graphics in the Text

With a few exceptions—such as cover illustrations used to grab attention—graphics should be accompanied by clear references within your text. Specifically, you should follow these rules:

- Include the graphic number in Arabic, not Roman numerals, when you are using more than one graphic.
- Include the title, and sometimes the page number, if either is needed for clarity or emphasis.
- Incorporate the reference smoothly into text wording.

Here are two ways to phrase and position a graphics reference. Example 1, includes the additional emphasis of the graphics title, whereas in Example 2, the title is left out. Also, note that you can draw more attention to the graphic by placing the reference at the start of the sentence in a separate clause. Or you can relegate the reference to a parenthetical expression at the end or middle of the passage. Choose the option that best suits your purposes.

- **Example 1:** In the past 5 years, 56 businesses in the county have started in-house recycling programs. The result has been a dramatic shift in the amount of property the county has bought for new waste sites, as shown in Figure 5 ("Landfill Purchases, 1996–2001").
- **Example 2:** As shown in Figure 5, the county has purchased much less land for landfills during the last 5 years. This dramatic reduction

results from the fact that 56 businesses have started in-house recycling programs.

## Graphics Guideline 2: Think about Where to Put Graphics

In most cases, locate a graphic close to the text in which it is mentioned. This immediate reinforcement of text by an illustration gives graphics their greatest strength. Variations of this option, as well as several other possibilities, are presented here:

- **Same page as text reference:** A simple visual, such as an informal table, should go on the same page as the text reference if you think it is too small for a separate page.
- **Page opposite text reference:** A complex graphic, such as a long table, that accompanies a specific page of text can go on the page opposite the text—that is, on the opposite page of a two-page spread. Usually this option is exercised *only* in documents that are printed on both sides of the paper throughout.
- **Page following first text reference:** Most text graphics appear on the page after the first reference. If the graphic is referred to throughout the text, it can be repeated at later points. (Note: Readers prefer to have graphics positioned exactly where they need them, rather than having to refer to another part of the document.)
- **Attachments or appendices:** Graphics can go at the end of the document in two cases: first, if the text contains so many references to the graphic that placement in a central location, such as an appendix, would make it more accessible; and second, if the graphic contains less important supporting material that would only interrupt the text.

## Graphics Guideline 3: Position Graphics Vertically When Possible

Readers prefer graphics they can view without having to turn the document sideways. However, if the table or figure cannot fit vertically on a standard $8\frac{1}{2}" \times 11"$ page, either use a foldout or place the graphic horizontally on the page. In the latter case, position the illustration so that the top is on the left margin. (In other words, the page must be turned clockwise to be viewed.)

## Graphics Guideline 4: Avoid Clutter

Let simplicity be your guide. Readers go to graphics for relief from, or reinforcement of, the text. They do not want to be bombarded by visual clutter. Omit information that is not relevant to your purpose, while still making the illustration clear and self-contained. Also, use enough white space so that the readers' eyes are drawn to the graphic. The final section of this chapter discusses graphics clutter in more detail.

### Graphics Guideline 5: Provide Titles, Notes, Keys, and Source Data

Graphics should be as self-contained and self-explanatory as possible. More-over, they must note any borrowed information. Follow these basic rules for format and acknowledgment of sources:

- **Title:** Follow the graphic number with a short, precise title—either on the line below the number *or* on the same line after a colon (for example, "Figure 3: Salary Scales").
- **Tables:** The number and title go at the top. (As noted in Table Guideline 1 on page 54, one exception is informal tables. They have no table number or title.)
- **Figures:** The number and title are normally placed below the illustration. Centre titles or place them flush with the left margin.
- **Notes for explanation:** When introductory information for the graphic is needed, place a note directly underneath the title *or* at the bottom of the graphic.
- **Keys or legends for simplicity:** If a graphic needs many labels, consider using a legend or key, which lists the labels and corresponding symbols on the graphic. For example, a pie chart might have the letters *A, B, C, D,* and *E* printed on the pie pieces, whereas a legend at the top, bottom, or side of the figure would list what the letters represent.
- **Source information at the bottom:** You have a moral, and sometimes legal, obligation to cite the person, organization, or publication from which you borrowed information for the figure. Either (1) precede the description with the word "Source" and a colon or (2) if you borrowed just part of a graphic, introduce the citation with "Adapted from."

Besides citing the source, it is sometimes necessary to request permission to use copyrighted or proprietary information, depending on your use and the amount you are borrowing. (A prominent exception is most informa-tion provided by the federal government. Most government publications are not copyrighted.) Consult a reference librarian for details about seek-ing permission.

## *Guidelines for Pie Charts*

Familiar to most readers, pie charts show relationships between the parts and the whole—when just approximate information is needed. Their simple cir-cles with clear labels can provide comforting simplicity within even the most complicated report. Yet, the simple form makes them less useful when you need to reveal detailed information. Here are specific guidelines for constructing pie charts.

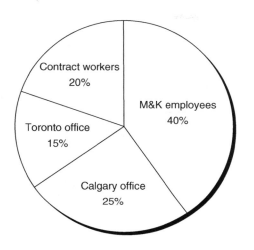

**FIGURE 3–2**
Pie chart with as few pieces
as possible

## Pie Chart Guideline 1: Use No More Than 10 Divisions

To make pie charts work well, limit the number of pie pieces to no more than 10. In fact, the fewer the better. This approach lets the reader grasp major relationships, without having to wade through the clutter of tiny divisions that are difficult to read. Figure 3–2, for example, aims to show how a large company will staff a particular project. The reader can quickly see that project staff will come from three main offices.

## Pie Chart Guideline 2: Move Clockwise from 12:00, from Largest to Smallest Wedge

Readers prefer pie charts oriented like a clock—with the first wedge starting at 12:00. Move from largest to smallest wedge to provide a convenient organizing principle.

Make exceptions to this design only for good reason. In Figure 3–2, for example, the last wedge, contract workers, represents a greater percentage than the previous wedge. In this way, it does not break up the sequence the writer wants to establish by grouping the two offices together.

## Pie Chart Guideline 3: Use Pie Charts Especially for Percentages and Money

Pie charts catch the reader's eye best when they represent items divisible by 100, as with percentages and dollars. Figure 3–2 shows percentages; Figure 3–3 on the next page shows money. Using the pie chart for money breakdowns is made even more appropriate by the coinlike shape of the chart.

**FIGURE 3–3**
Pie chart showing money breakdown for average deductions
from an M&K paycheque

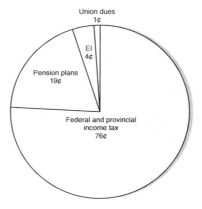

Source: *Technical Writing: A Practical Approach,* 3rd Canadian Edition (p. 377) by W. S. Pfeiffer
and J. Boogerd, 2004. Reprinted with permission by Pearson Education Canada Inc.

## Pie Chart Guideline 4: Be Creative, but Stay Simple
Figure 3–4 on the next page shows how you can emphasize one piece of
the pie:

1. Shade a wedge
2. Remove a wedge from the main pie
3. Place related pie charts in a three-dimensional drawing

Today's graphics software packages can create these and other variations
for you, so experiment a bit. Of course, always make sure to keep your charts
from becoming too detailed. Pie charts should stay simple.

## Pie Chart Guideline 5: Draw and Label Carefully
The most common pie chart errors are (1) wedge sizes that do not correspond
correctly to percentages or money amounts and (2) pie sizes that are too
small to accommodate the information placed in them. Here are some suggestions for avoiding these mistakes:

- **Pie size:** Make sure the chart occupies enough of the page. On a standard
  21.5 cm × 27.9 cm sheet with only one pie chart, your circle should be
  from 7.6 cm to 15.2 cm in diameter—large enough not to be dwarfed by
  labels and small enough to leave sufficient white space in the margins.
- **Labels:** Place the wedge labels either inside the pie or outside, depending
  on the number of wedges, the number of wedge labels, or the length of the
  labels. Choose the option that produces the cleanest-looking chart.
- **Conversion of percentages:** If you are drawing the pie chart by hand, not
  using a computer program, use a protractor or similar device. One percent
  of the pie equals 3.6 degrees (3.6 × 100% = 360 degrees in a circle). With
  that formula as your guide, you can convert percentages or cents to degrees.

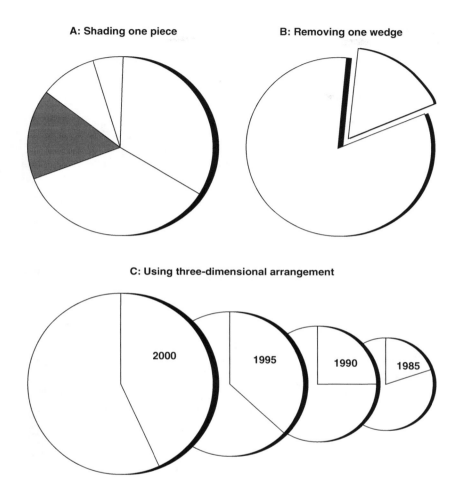

**A: Shading one piece**

**B: Removing one wedge**

**C: Using three-dimensional arrangement**

2000

1995

1990

1985

**FIGURE 3–4**
Techniques for emphasis in pie charts

Remember, however, that a pie chart does not reveal fine distinctions very well; it is best used for showing larger differences.

## Guidelines for Bar Charts

Like pie charts, bar charts are easily recognized, for they are seen every day in newspapers and magazines. Unlike pie charts, however, bar charts can accommodate a good deal of technical detail. Comparisons are provided by means of two or more bars running either horizontally or vertically on the page. Follow these five guidelines to create effective bar charts.

## Bar Chart Guideline 1: Use a Limited Number of Bars

Although bar charts can show more information than pie charts, both types of illustrations have their limits. Bar charts begin to break down when there are so many bars that information is not easily grasped. The maximum bar number can vary according to chart size, of course. Figure 3–5 shows several

**FIGURE 3–5**
Bar charts

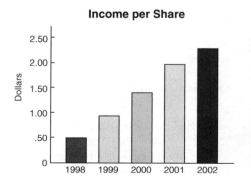

multibar charts. The impact of the charts is enhanced by the limited number of bars.

## Bar Chart Guideline 2: Show Comparisons Clearly

Bar lengths should be varied enough to show comparisons quickly and clearly. Avoid using bars that are too close in length, for then readers must study the chart before understanding it. Such a chart lacks immediate visual impact.

Also, avoid the opposite tendency of using bar charts to show data that are much different in magnitude. To relate such differences, some writers resort to the dubious technique of inserting "break lines" (two parallel lines) on an axis to reflect breaks in scale (see Figure 3–6). Although this approach at least reminds readers of the breaks, it is still deceptive. For example, note that Figure 3–6 provides no *visual* demonstration of the relationship between 50 and 2,800. The reader must think about these differences before making sense out of the chart. In other words, the use of hash marks runs counter to a main goal of graphics—creating an immediate and accurate visual impact.

## Bar Chart Guideline 3: Keep Bar Widths Equal and Adjust Space between Bars Carefully

Although bar length varies, bar width must remain constant. As for distance between the bars, following are three options (along with examples in Figure 3–7 on the next page):

- **Option A: Use no space** when there are close comparisons or many bars, so that differences are easier to grasp.
- **Option B: Use equal space, but less than bar width** when bar height differences are great enough to be seen in spite of the distance between bars.
- **Option C: Use variable space** when gaps between some bars are needed to reflect gaps in the data.

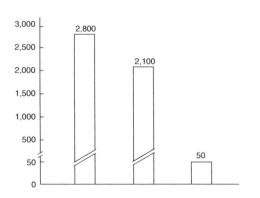

**FIGURE 3–6**
Hash marks on bar charts—a technique that can lead to misunderstanding

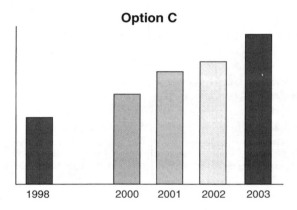

**FIGURE 3–7**
Bar chart variations

## Bar Chart Guideline 4: Carefully Arrange the Order of Bars

The arrangement of bars is what reveals meaning to readers. Here are two common approaches:

- **Sequential:** used when the progress of the bars shows a trend—for example, a company's increasing number of environmental projects in the last five years
- **Ascending or descending order:** used when you want to make a point by the rising or falling of the bars—for example, the 1999 profits of a company's six international offices, from lowest to highest

## Bar Chart Guideline 5: Be Creative

Figure 3–8 on the ext page shows two bar chart variations that help display multiple trends. The *segmented bars* in Option A produce two types of

**FIGURE 3–8**
Bar chart variations for multiple trends

information: the total sales (A + B + C) and the individual sales for A, B, and C. The *grouped bars* in Option B show the individual sales trends for D, F, and G, along with a comparison of all three by year. Note that the amounts are written on the bars to highlight comparisons.

Although these and other bar chart variations may be useful, remember to retain the basic simplicity of the chart.

## Guidelines for Line Charts

Line charts are a common graphic. Almost every newspaper contains a few charts covering topics such as stock trends, car prices, or weather. More than other graphics, line charts telegraph complex trends immediately.

They work by using vertical and horizontal axes to reflect quantities of two different variables. The vertical (or *y*) axis usually plots the dependent variable; the horizontal (or *x*) axis usually plots the independent variable. (The dependent variable is affected by changes in the independent variable.) Lines then connect points that have been plotted on the chart. When using line charts, follow these five main guidelines:

### Line Chart Guideline 1: Use Line Charts for Trends

Readers are affected by the direction and angle of the chart's line(s), so take advantage of this persuasive potential. In Figure 3–9, on the next page for example, the writer wants to show the feasibility of adopting a new medical plan. Including a line chart in the study gives immediate emphasis to the

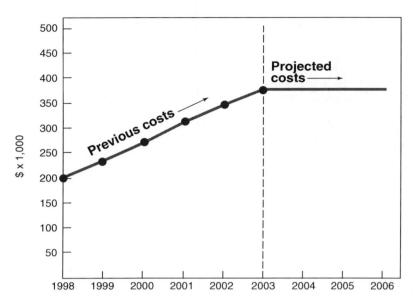

**FIGURE 3–9**
Line chart used to show effect of proposed medical plan

most important issue—the effect the new plan would have on stabilizing the firm's medical costs.

## Line Chart Guideline 2: Locate Line Charts with Care

Given their strong impact, line charts can be especially useful as attention-grabbers. Consider placing them (1) on cover pages (to engage reader interest in the document), (2) at the beginning of sections that describe trends, and (3) in conclusions (to reinforce a major point of your document).

## Line Chart Guideline 3: Strive for Accuracy and Clarity

Like bar charts, line charts can be misused or just poorly constructed. Be sure that the line or lines on the graph truly reflect the data you have used. Also, select a scale that does not mislead readers with visual gimmicks. Here are some specific suggestions to keep your line charts accurate and clear:

- Start all scales from zero to eliminate the possible confusion of breaks in amounts (see Bar Chart Guideline 2).
- Select a vertical-to-horizontal ratio for axis lengths that is pleasing to the eye (three vertical to four horizontal is common).
- Make chart lines as thick as, or thicker than, the axis lines.
- Use shading under the line when it will make the chart more readable.

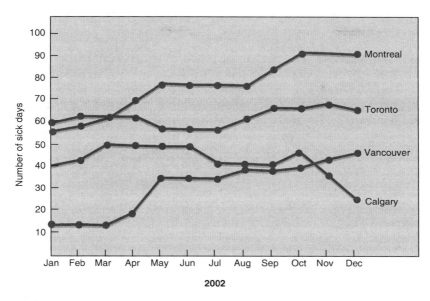

**FIGURE 3–10**
Line chart using multiple lines to show number of sick days taken at four offices: 2002
Adapted from William S. Pfeiffer, *Proposal Writing* (Columbus, OH: Merrill, 1989), p. 152.

## Line Chart Guideline 4: Do Not Place Numbers on the Chart Itself

Line charts derive their main effect from the simplicity of lines that show trends. Avoid cluttering the chart with a lot of numbers that only detract from the visual impact.

## Line Chart Guideline 5: Use Multiple Lines with Care

Like bar charts, line charts can show multiple trends. Simply add another line or two. If you place too many lines on one chart, however, you run the risk of confusing the reader with too much data. Use no more than four or five lines on a single chart (see Figure 3–10).

## Guidelines for Tables

Tables present readers with raw data, usually in the form of numbers but sometimes in the form of words. Tables are classified as either formal or informal:

- **Informal tables:** limited data arranged in the form of either rows or columns
- **Formal tables:** data arranged in a grid, always with both horizontal rows and vertical columns

These five guidelines will help you design and position tables within the text of your documents.

### Table Guideline 1: Use Informal Tables as Extensions of Text

Informal tables are usually merged with the text on a page, rather than isolated on a separate page or attachment. As such, an informal table usually has (1) no table number or title, (2) no listing in the list of illustrations in a formal report or proposal, and (3) few if any headings for rows or columns.

**Example:**
Our project in Alberta, will involve engineers, technicians, and salespeople from three offices, in these numbers:

| | |
|---|---|
| Toronto Office | 45 |
| Montreal Office | 34 |
| Calgary Office | 6 |
| Total | 85 |

### Table Guideline 2: Use Formal Tables for Complex Data Separated from Text

Formal tables may appear on the page of text that includes the table reference, on the page following the first text reference, or in an attachment or appendix. In any case, you should do the following:

- Extract important data from the table and highlight them in the text.
- Make every formal table as clear and visually appealing as possible.

### Table Guideline 3: Use Plenty of White Space

Used around and within tables, white space guides the eye through a table much better than do black lines. Avoid putting complete boxes around tables. Instead, leave one inch more of white space than you would normally leave around text.

### Table Guideline 4: Follow Usual Conventions Dividing and Explaining Data

Figure 3–11 on the next page shows a typical formal table. It satisfies the overriding goal of being clear and self-contained. To achieve such an objective in your tables, follow these guidelines:

1. **Titles and numberings:** Give a title to each formal table, and place title and number above the table. Number each table if the document contains two or more tables.
2. **Headings:** Create short, clear headings for all columns and rows.
3. **Abbreviations:** Include in the headings any necessary abbreviations or symbols, such as *kg* or %. Spell out abbreviations and define terms in a key or footnote if any reader may need such assistance.

### TABLE 6: M&K Employee Retirement Fund

| Investment Type | Book Value | Market Value | % of Total Market Value |
|---|---|---|---|
| Temporary Securities | $ 434,084 | $ 434,084 | 18.6% |
| Bonds | 679,081 | 842,056 | 36.0 |
| Common Stocks | 508,146 | 39,350 | 44.5 |
| Mortgages | 18,063 | 18,063 | .9 |
| Real Estate | 1,939 | 1,939 | nil |
| Totals | $1,641,313 | $2,335,492 | 100.0% |

Note: This table contrasts the book value versus the market value of the M & K Employee Retirement Fund, as of December 31, 2003.

**FIGURE 3–11**
Example of formal table

4. **Numbers:** Round off numbers when possible, for ease of reading. Also, align multidigit numbers on the right edge, or at the decimal when shown.
5. **Notes:** Place any necessary explanatory headnotes either between the title and the table (if the notes are short) *or* at the bottom of the table.
6. **Footnotes:** Place any necessary footnotes below the table.
7. **Sources:** Place any necessary source references below the footnotes.
8. **Caps:** Use uppercase and lowercase letters, rather than full caps.

### Table Guideline 5: Pay Special Attention to Cost Data

Most readers prefer to have complicated financial information placed in tabular form. Given the importance of such data, edit cost tables with great care. Devote extra attention to these two issues:

- Placement of decimals in costs
- Correct totals of figures

Documents like proposals can be considered contracts in some courts of law, so there is no room for error in relating costs.

## Guidelines for Technical Drawings

Technical drawings are important tools for companies that produce or use technical products. These drawings can accompany documents such as instructions, reports, sales orders, proposals, brochures, and posters. They are preferred over photographs when specific views are more important than photographic detail. Drawings used to be produced mainly by hand, but now they are usually created by computer-assisted design (CAD) systems. Follow these guidelines for producing technical drawings that complement your text.

### Drawing Guideline 1: Choose the Right Amount of Detail

Keep drawings as simple as possible. Use only that level of detail that serves the purpose of your document and satisfies your reader's needs. For example, Figure 3–12 will be used in a brochure on maintaining home heating systems. Its intention is to focus on one part of the thermostat—the lever and attached roller. Completed on a CAD system, this drawing presents an exploded view so that the location of the arm can be seen easily.

### Drawing Guideline 2: Label Parts Well

A common complaint of drawings is that parts included in the illustration are not carefully or clearly labelled. Place labels on every part you want your

**FIGURE 3–12**
Technical drawing (exploded view) of home thermostat

reader to see. (Conversely, you can choose *not* to label those parts that are irrelevant to your purpose.)

When you label parts, use a typeface large enough for easy reading. Also, arrange labels so that (1) they are as easy as possible for your reader to locate and (2) they do not detract from the importance of the drawing itself. The simple labelling in Figure 3–12 fulfills these objectives.

## Drawing Guideline 3: Choose the Most Appropriate View

As already noted, illustrations—unlike photographs—permit you to choose the level of detail needed. In addition, drawings offer you a number of options for perspective or view:

- **Exterior view** shows surface features with either a two- or three-dimensional appearance—see Figure 3–13.

Tube Length: 58.8 in.
Tube Weight: 788 lbs.
Material: Bronze
Bore: 4.62 in.
Range: 1072 yd. (0.81 mi.)
Purpose: Standard U.S. field gun of the Civil War

**FIGURE 3–13**
Technical drawing using CAD system

- **Cross-section view** shows a "slice" of the object so that interiors can be viewed.
- **Exploded view**  shows relationship of parts to each other by "exploding" the mechanism—see Figure 3–12.
- **Cutaway view**  shows inner workings of object by removing part of the exterior.

### Drawing Guideline 4: Use Legends When There Are Many Parts

In complex drawings, avoid cluttering the illustration with many labels. Figure 3–13, for example, places all labels in one easy-to-find spot, rather than leaving them on the drawing.

## ORAL PRESENTATIONS

Oral presentations, or speeches, are defined quite broadly. Usually they can be classified according to criteria such as these:

1. **Format:**  from informal question-and-answer sessions to formal speeches
2. **Length:**  from several-minute overviews to long sessions of an hour or more
3. **Number of presenters:**  from solo performances to group presentations
4. **Content:**  from a few highlights to detailed coverage

   Throughout your career, you will speak to different-sized groups, on diverse topics, and in varied formats. The following sections provide some common guidelines on preparation and delivery, graphics, and overcoming nervousness.

## Guidelines for Preparation and Delivery

The goal of most oral presentations is quite simple: You must present a few basic points, in a fairly brief time, to an interested but usually impatient audience. Simplicity, brevity, and interest are the keys to success. If you deliver what *you* expect when *you* hear a speech, then you will give good presentations yourself.

### Speech Guideline 1: Know Your Listeners

These features are common to most listeners:

- They cannot "rewind the tape" of your presentation, as opposed to the way they can skip back and forth through the text of a report.

- They are impatient after the first few minutes, particularly if they do not know where a speech is going.
- They will daydream and often need their attention brought back to the matter at hand (expect a 30-second attention span).
- They have heard so many disappointing presentations that they might not have high expectations for yours.

To respond to these realities, you must learn as much as possible about your listeners. For example, you can (1) consider what you already know about your audience, (2) talk with colleagues who have spoken to the same group, and (3) find out which listeners make the decisions.

Most important, make sure not to talk over anyone's head. If there are several levels of technical expertise represented by the group, find the lowest common denominator and decrease the technical level of your presentation accordingly. Remember—decision makers are often the ones without current technical experience. They may want only highlights. Later they can review written documents for details or solicit more technical information during the question-and-answer session after you speak.

### Speech Guideline 2: Use the Preacher's Maxim
The well-known preacher's maxim goes like this:

> First you tell 'em what you're gonna tell 'em, then you tell 'em, and then you tell 'em what you told 'em.

Why should most speakers follow this plan? Because it gives the speech a simple three-part structure that listeners can grasp easily. Here is how your speech should be organized (note that it corresponds to the ABC format used throughout this text for writing):

**1. Abstract (beginning of presentation):** Right at the outset, you should (1) get the listeners' interest (with an anecdote, a statistic, or other technique), (2) state the exact purpose of the speech, and (3) list the main points you will cover. Do not try the patience of your audience with an extended introduction. Use no more than a minute.

Example: "Last year, Jones Engineering had 56 percent more field accidents than the year before. This morning, I'll examine a proposed safety plan that aims to solve this problem. My presentation will focus on three main benefits of the new plan: lower insurance premiums, less lost time from accidents, and better morale among the employees."

**2. Body (middle of presentation):** Here you discuss the points mentioned briefly in the introduction, in the same order that they were mentioned. Provide the kinds of obvious transitions that help your listeners stay on track.

Example: "The final benefit of the new safety plan will be improved morale among the fieldworkers at all our job sites. . . ."

**3.  Conclusion (end of presentation):**  In the conclusion, review the main ideas covered in the body of the speech and specify actions you want to occur as a result of your presentation.

Example: "Jones Engineering can benefit from this new safety plan in three main ways. . . . If Jones implements the new plan next month, I believe you will see a dramatic reduction in on-site accidents during the last half of the year."

This simple three-part plan for all presentations gives listeners the handle they need to understand your speech. First, there is a clear "road map" in the introduction so that they know what lies ahead in the rest of the speech. Second, there is an organized pattern in the body, with clear transitions between points. And third, there is a strong finish that brings the audience back full circle to the main thrust of the presentation.

## Speech Guideline 3: Stick to a Few Main Points

Our short-term memory holds limited items. It follows that listeners are most attentive to speeches organized around a few major points. In fact, a good argument can be made for organizing information in groups of *threes* whenever possible. For reasons that are not totally understood, listeners seem to remember groups of three items more than they do any other size groupings—perhaps for these reasons:

- The number is simple.
- It parallels the overall three-part structure of most speeches and documents (beginning, middle, end).
- Many good speakers have used triads (Winston Churchill's "Blood, sweat, and tears," Caesar's "I came, I saw, I conquered," etc.).

Whatever the reason, groupings of three will make your speech more memorable to the audience.

## Speech Guideline 4: Put Your Outline on Cards, Paper, or Overheads

The best presentations are "extemporaneous," meaning the speaker shows great familiarity with the material but uses notes for occasional reference. Avoid the extremes of (1) reading a speech verbatim, which many listeners consider the ultimate insult, or (2) memorizing a speech, which can make your presentation seem somewhat wooden and artificial.

Ironically, you appear more natural if you refer to notes during a presentation. Such extemporaneous speaking allows you to make last-minute changes in phrasing and emphasis that may improve delivery, rather than locking you into specific phrasing that is memorized or written out word for word.

Depending on your personal preference, you may choose to write speech notes on (1) index cards, (2) a sheet or two of paper, or (3) overhead transparencies. The main advantages and disadvantages of each are listed in Figure 3–14.

---

**1. *Notes on Cards (7.6 cm × 12.7 cm or 10.1 cm × 15.2 cm)***

Advantages

- Are easy to carry in a shirt pocket, coat, or bag
- Provide way to organize points, through ordering of cards
- Can lead to smooth delivery in that each card contains only one or two points that are easy to view
- Can be held in one hand, allowing you to move away from lectern while speaking

Disadvantages

- Keep you from viewing outline of entire speech
- Require that you flip through cards repeatedly in speech
- Can limit use of gestures with hands
- Can cause confusion if they are not in correct order

**2. *Notes on Sheets of Paper***

Advantages

- Help you quickly view outline of entire speech
- Leave your hands free to use gestures
- Are less obvious than note cards, for no flipping is needed

Disadvantages

- Tend to tie you to lectern, where the sheets lie
- May cause slipups in delivery if you lose your place on the page

**3. *Notes on Overhead Transparencies***

Advantages

- Introduce variety to audience
- Give visual reinforcement to audience
- Can be turned on and off

Disadvantages

- Cannot be altered as easily at last minute
- Must be presented neatly and in parallel style
- Involve the usual risks that reliance on machinery always introduces into your presentation

---

**FIGURE 3–14**
Speech notes

## Speech Guideline 5: Practise, Practise, Practise

Many speakers prepare a well-organized speech but then fail to add the essential ingredient: practice. Constant practice distinguishes superior presentations from mediocre ones. It also helps to eliminate the nervousness that most speakers feel at one time or another.

In practising your presentation, make use of four main techniques. They are listed here, from least effective to most effective:

- **Practise before a mirror:** This old-fashioned approach allows you to hear and see yourself in action. The drawback, of course, is that it is difficult to evaluate your own performance while you are speaking. Nevertheless, such run-throughs definitely make you more comfortable with the material.
- **Use of audiotape:** Most presenters have access to a tape player, so this approach is quite practical. The portability of the machine allows you to practise almost anywhere. Although taping a presentation will not improve gestures, it will help you discover and eliminate verbal distractions such as filler words *(uhhhh, um, ya know)*.
- **Use of live audience:** Groups of your colleagues, friends, or family—simulating a real audience—can provide the kinds of responses that approximate those of a real audience. In setting up this type of practice session, however, make certain that observers understand the criteria for a good presentation and are prepared to give an honest, forthright critique.
- **Use of videotape:** This practice technique allows you to see and hear yourself as others do. Your careful review of the tape, particularly when done with another qualified observer, can help you identify and eliminate problems with posture, eye contact, vocal patterns, and gestures. At first it can be a chilling experience, but soon you will get over the awkwardness of seeing yourself on film.

## Speech Guideline 6: Speak Vigorously and Deliberately

"Vigorously" means with enthusiasm; "deliberately" means with care, attention, and appropriate emphasis on words and phrases. The importance of this guideline becomes clear when you think back to how you felt during the last speech you heard. At the very least, you expected the speaker to show interest in the subject and to demonstrate enthusiasm. Good information is not enough. You need to arouse the interest of the listeners.

You may wonder, "How much enthusiasm is enough?" The best way to answer this question is to hear or (preferably) watch yourself on tape. Your delivery should incorporate just enough enthusiasm so that it sounds and looks a bit unnatural to you. Few if any listeners ever complain about a speech being too enthusiastic or a speaker being too energetic. But many, many people complain about dull speakers who fail to show that they themselves are excited about the topic. Remember—every presentation is, in a sense, "show time."

## Speech Guideline 7: Avoid Filler Words

Avoiding filler words presents a tremendous challenge to most speakers. When they think about what comes next or encounter a break in the speech, they may tend to fill the gap with filler words and phrases such as these:

uhhhhh . . .

ya know . . .

okay . . .

well . . . uh . . .

like . . .

I mean . . .

umm . . .

These gap-fillers are a bit like spelling errors in written work: Once your listeners find a few, they start looking for more and are distracted from your presentation. To eliminate such distractions, follow these three steps:

**Step 1: Use pauses to your advantage.** Short gaps or pauses inform the listener that you are shifting from one point to another. In signalling a transition, a pause draws attention to the point you make right after the pause. Note how listeners look at you when you pause. Do *not* fill these strategic pauses with filler words.

**Step 2: Practise with tape.** Tape is brutally honest: When you play it back, you will become instantly aware of fillers that occur more than once or twice. Keep a tally sheet of the fillers you use and their frequency. Your goal will be to reduce this frequency with every practice session.

**Step 3: Ask for help from others.** After working with tape machines in Step 2, give your speech to an individual who has been instructed to stop you after each filler. This technique gives immediate reinforcement.

## Speech Guideline 8: Use Rhetorical Questions

Enthusiasm, of course, is your best delivery technique for capturing the attention of the audience. Another technique is the use of rhetorical questions at pivotal points in your presentation.

Rhetorical questions are those you ask to get listeners thinking about a topic, not those that you would expect them to answer out loud. They prod listeners to think about your point and set up an expectation that important information will follow. Also, they break the monotony of standard declarative sentence patterns. For example, here is a rhetorical question used by a computer salesperson in proposing a purchase:

> I've discussed the three main advantages that a centralized word-processing centre would provide your office staff. But is this an approach that you can afford at this point in the company's growth?

Then the speaker would follow the question with remarks supporting the position that the system is affordable.

"What if" scenarios provide another way to introduce rhetorical questions. They gain the listeners' attention by having them envision a situation that might occur. For example, a safety engineer could use this kind of rhetorical question in proposing asbestos-removal services to a regional bank:

> What if you repossessed a building that contained dangerous levels of asbestos?
> Do you think that your bank would then be liable for removing all the asbestos?

Again, the question pattern heightens listener interest.

Rhetorical questions do not come naturally. You must make a conscious effort to insert them at points when it is most important to gain or redirect the attention of the audience. Three particularly effective uses follow:

1. **As a grabber at the beginning of a speech:** "Have you ever wondered how you might improve the productivity of your word-processing staff?"
2. **As a transition between major points:** "We've seen that centralized word processing can improve the speed of report production, but will it require any additions to your staff?"
3. **As an attention-getter right before your conclusion:** "Now that we've examined the features of centralized word processing, what's the next step you should make?"

## Speech Guideline 9: Maintain Eye Contact

Your main goal—always—is to keep listeners interested in what you are saying. This goal requires that you maintain control, using whatever techniques you can employ to direct the attention of the audience. Frequent eye contact is one good strategy.

The simple truth is that listeners pay closer attention to what you are saying when you look at them. Think how you react when a speaker makes constant eye contact with you. If you are like most people, you feel as if the speaker is speaking to you personally—even if there are 100 people in the audience. Also, you tend to feel more obligated to listen when you know that the speaker's eyes will be meeting yours throughout the presentation. Here are some ways you can make eye contact a natural part of your own strategy for effective oral presentations:

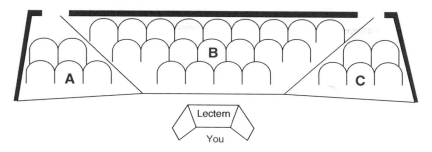

**FIGURE 3–15**
Audience sections

- **With audiences of about 30 or less:** Make regular eye contact with everyone in the room. Be particularly careful not to ignore members of the audience who are seated to your far right and far left (see Figure 3–15). Many speakers tend to focus on the listeners within Section B. Instead, make wide sweeps so that listeners in Sections A and C get equal attention.
- **With large audiences:** There may be too many people or a room too large for you to make individual eye contact with all listeners. In this case, focus on just a few people in all three sections of the audience noted in Figure 3–15. This approach gives the appearance that you are making eye contact with the entire audience.
- **With any size audience:** Occasionally look away from the audience— either to your notes or toward a part of the room where there are no faces looking back. In this way, you avoid the appearance of staring too intensely at your audience. Also, these breaks give you the chance to collect your thoughts or check your notes.

## Speech Guideline 10: Use Appropriate Gestures and Posture
Speaking is only one part of giving a speech; another is adopting appropriate posture and using gestures that will reinforce what you are saying. Note that good speakers are much more than "talking heads" before a lectern. Instead, they do the following:

1. Use their hands and fingers to emphasize major points
2. Stand straight, without leaning on or gripping the lectern
3. Step out from behind the lectern on occasion, to decrease the distance to the audience
4. Point toward visuals on screens or charts, without losing eye contact with the audience

The audience will judge you by what you say *and* what they see, a fact that again makes videotaping a crucial part of your preparation. With work on this facet of your presentation, you can avoid problems like keeping your hands constantly in your pockets, rustling change (remove pocket change and keys beforehand), tapping a pencil, scratching nervously, slouching over a lectern, and shifting from foot to foot.

## Guidelines for Speech Graphics

More than ever before, listeners expect good graphics during oral presentations. Much like gestures, graphics transform the words of your presentation into true communication with the audience. The following 10 guidelines will help you use graphics to enhance each speech.

### Speech Graphics Guideline 1: Discover Listener Preferences

Some professionals prefer simple speech graphics, such as a conventional flip chart. Others prefer more sophisticated equipment, such as video projectors connected to laptop computers. For example, if your instructor in this course uses presentation graphics, he or she may have chosen overhead transparencies *or* a PowerPoint program.

Your listeners are usually willing to indicate their preferences when you call on them. Contact the audience ahead of time and make some inquiries. Also, ask for information about the room in which you will be speaking. If possible, request a setting that allows you to make best use of your graphics choice. If you have no control over the setting, then choose graphics that best fit the constraints. Details about lighting, wall space, and chair configuration can greatly influence your selection.

### Speech Graphics Guideline 2: Think about Graphics Early

Graphics done as an afterthought usually look "tacked on." Plan graphics while you prepare the text so that the final presentation will seem fluid. This guideline holds true especially if you rely upon specialists to prepare your visuals. These professionals need some lead time to do their best work. Also, they can often provide helpful insights about how visuals will enhance the presentation—*if* you consult them early enough and *if* you make them a part of your presentation team.

The goal is to use graphics of which you can be proud. Never, never put yourself in the position of having to apologize for the quality of your graphic material. If an illustration is not up to the quality your audience would expect, do *not* use it.

### Speech Graphics Guideline 3: Keep the Message Simple

Listeners may be suspicious of slick visual effects that appear to subordinate the content of the speech. Many prefer the simplicity of simple overhead transparencies and flip charts. However, you may prefer to use PowerPoint, video, or other high-tech graphics.

### Speech Graphics Guideline 4: Make Any Wording Brief and Visible

Some basic design guidelines apply whether you are using posters, overhead transparencies, or computer-aided graphics such as PowerPoint.

- Use few words, emphasizing just one idea on each frame.
- Use much white space, perhaps as much as 60 to 70 percent per frame.
- Use "landscape" format more often than "portrait," especially since it is the preferred default setting for most presentation software.
- Use sans serif large print, from 14 to 18 pt. minimum for text to 48 pt. for titles.

Your goal should be to create graphics that are easily seen from anywhere in the room and that complement—but do not overpower—your presentation.

### Speech Graphics Guideline 5: Use Colours Carefully

Colours can add flair to visuals. Follow these simple guidelines to make colours work for you:

- Have a good reason for using colour (such as the need to highlight three different bars on a graph with three distinct colours).
- Use only dark, easily seen colours, and be sure that a colour contrasts with its background (for example, yellow on white would not work well).
- Use no more than three or four colours in each graphic (to avoid a confused effect).
- For variety, consider using white on a black or dark green background.

### Speech Graphics Guideline 6: Leave Up Graphics Long Enough

Because graphics reinforce text, they should be shown only while you address the particular point at hand. For example, reveal a graph just as you are saying, "As you can see from the graph, the projected revenue reaches a peak in 2005." Then pause and leave up the graph a bit longer for the audience to absorb your point.

How long is *too* long? A graphic outlives its usefulness when it remains in sight after you have moved on to another topic. Listeners will continue to study it and ignore what you are now saying. If you use a graphic once and plan to return to it, take it down after its first use and show it again later.

### Speech Graphics Guideline 7: Avoid Handouts

Because timing is so important in your use of speech graphics, handouts are usually a bad idea. Readers move through a handout at their own pace, rather than at the pace the speaker might prefer. Thus, handouts cause you to lose the attention of your audience. Use them only if (1) no other visual will do, (2) your listener has requested them, or (3) you distribute them as reference material *after* you have finished talking.

### Speech Graphics Guideline 8: Maintain Eye Contact While Using Graphics

Do not stare at your visuals while you speak. Maintain control of listeners' responses by looking back and forth from the visual to faces in the audience. To point to the graphic aid, use the hand closest to the visual. Using the opposite hand causes you to cross over your torso, forcing you to turn your neck and head away from the audience.

### Speech Graphics Guideline 9: Include All Graphics in Your Practice Sessions

Dry runs before the actual presentation should include every graphic you plan to use, in its final form. This is a good reason to prepare graphics as you prepare text, rather than as an afterthought. Running through a final practice without graphics would be much like doing a dress rehearsal for a play without costumes and props—you would be leaving out parts that require the greatest degree of timing and orchestration. Practising with graphics helps you improve transitions.

### Speech Graphics Guideline 10: Use Your Own Equipment

Murphy's Law always seems to apply when you use another person's audiovisual equipment: Whatever can go wrong, will. For example, a new bulb burns out, there is no extra bulb in the equipment drawer, an extension cord is too short, the screen does not stay down, the client's computer doesn't read your disk—many speakers have experienced these problems and more. Even if the equipment works, it often operates differently from what you are used to. The only sure way to put the odds in your favour is to carry your own equipment and set it up in advance.

However, most of us have to rely on someone else's equipment at least sometimes. Here are a few ways to ward off disaster:

- Find out exactly who will be responsible for providing the equipment and contact that person in advance.
- Have some easy-to-carry backup supplies in your car—an extension cord, an overhead projector bulb, felt-tip markers, and chalk, for example.
- Bring handout versions of your visuals to use as a last resort.

In short, you want to avoid putting yourself in the position of having to apologize. Plan well.

## *Guidelines for Overcoming Nervousness*

The problem of nervousness deserves special mention because it is so common. Virtually everyone who gives speeches feels some degree of nervousness before "the event." An instinctive "fight or flight" response kicks in for the many people who have an absolute dread of presentations. As the cliché goes, do not try to eliminate "butterflies" before a presentation—just get them to fly in formation. It is best to acknowledge that a certain degree of nervousness will always remain. Then go about the business of getting it to work for you. Here are a few suggestions.

### No Nerves Guideline 1: Know Your Speech

The most obvious suggestion is also the most important one. If you prepare your speech well, your command of the material will help to conquer any queasiness you feel—particularly at the beginning of the speech, when nervousness is usually at its peak. Be so sure of the material that your listeners will overlook any initial discomfort you may feel.

### No Nerves Guideline 2: Prepare Yourself Physically

Your physical well-being before the speech can have a direct bearing on anxiety. More than ever before, most cultures understand the essential connection between mental and physical well-being. This connection suggests you should take these precautions before your presentation:

- **Avoid caffeine or alcohol for at least several hours before you speak.** You do not need the additional jitters brought on by caffeine or the false sense of ease brought on by alcohol.
- **Eat a light, well-balanced meal within a few hours of speaking.** However, do not overdo it—particularly if a meal comes right before your speech. If you are convinced that any eating will increase your anxiety, wait to eat until after speaking.
- **Practise deep-breathing exercises before you speak.** Inhale and exhale slowly, making your body slow down to a pace you can control. If you can control your breathing, you can probably keep the butterflies flying in formation.
- **Exercise normally the same day of the presentation.** A good walk will help invigorate you and reduce nervousness. However, do not wear yourself out by exercising more than you would normally.

### No Nerves Guideline 3: Picture Yourself Giving a Great Presentation

Many speakers become nervous because their imaginations are working overtime. They envision the kinds of failures that almost never occur.

Instead, speakers should be constantly bombarding their psyches with images of success, not failure. Mentally take yourself through the following steps of the presentation:

- Arriving at the room
- Feeling comfortable at your chair
- Getting encouraging looks from your audience
- Giving an attention-getting introduction
- Presenting your supporting points with clarity and smoothness
- Ending with an effective wrap-up
- Fielding questions with confidence

Sometimes called "imaging," this technique helps to program success into your thinking and to control negative feelings that pass through the minds of even the best speakers.

### No Nerves Guideline 4: Arrange the Room as You Want

To control your anxiety, assert some control over the physical environment as well. You need everything going for you if you are to feel at ease. Make sure that chairs are arranged to your satisfaction, that the lectern is positioned to your taste, that the lighting is adequate, and so on. These features of the setting can almost always be adjusted if you make the effort to ask. Again, it is a matter of your asserting control to increase your overall confidence.

### No Nerves Guideline 5: Have a Glass of Water Nearby

Extreme thirst and a dry throat are physical symptoms of nervousness that can affect delivery. There is nothing to worry about as long as you have water available. Think about this need ahead of time so that you do not have to interrupt your presentation to pour a glass of water.

### No Nerves Guideline 6: Engage in Casual Banter before the Speech

If you have the opportunity, chat with members of the audience before the speech. This ice-breaking technique will reduce your nervousness and help start your relationship with the audience.

### No Nerves Guideline 7: Remember That You Are the Expert

As a final "psyching up" exercise before you speak, remind yourself that you have been invited or hired to speak on a topic about which you have useful knowledge. Your listeners want to hear what you have to say and are eager for you to provide useful information to them. So tell yourself, "I'm the expert here!"

## No Nerves Guideline 8: Do Not Admit Nervousness to the Audience

No matter how anxious you may feel, never admit it to others. First of all, you do not want listeners to feel sorry for you—that is not an emotion that will lead to a positive critique of your speech. Second, nervousness is almost never apparent to the audience. Your heart may be pounding, your knees may be shaking, and your throat may be dry, but few if any members of the audience can see these symptoms. Why draw attention to the problem by admitting to it? Third, you can best defeat initial anxiety by simply pushing on.

## No Nerves Guideline 9: Slow Down

Some speakers who feel nervous tend to speed through their presentations. If you have prepared well and practised the speech on tape, you are not likely to let this happen. Having heard yourself on tape, you will be better able to sense that the pace is too quick. As you speak, constantly remind yourself to maintain an appropriate pace. If you have had this problem before, you might even write "Slow down!" in the margin of your notes.

## No Nerves Guideline 10: Join a Speaking Organization

The previous nine guidelines will help reduce your anxiety about a particular speech. To help solve the problem over the long term, however, consider joining an organization like Toastmasters International, which promotes the speaking skills of all its members. Like some other speech organizations, Toastmasters has chapters that meet at many companies and campuses. These meetings provide an excellent, supportive environment in which all members can refine their speaking skills.

# Appendix A: ABC
# Formats and Examples

*C*hapter 2 covered the ABC format (Abstract/Body/Conclusion) in general. This appendix gets down to specifics by applying the ABC format to 16 on-the-job documents. You can use this section as a desk reference while outlining and writing your draft.

Each of the 16 sections contains two parts: (1) an ABC outline for the document, along with some "Helpful Hints" at the bottom of the page, and (2) a document example that follows the outline. Documents are provided for the following ABC models:

1. Positive letter
2. Negative letter
3. Neutral letter
4. Sales letter
5. Memorandum
6. Instructions
7. Problem analysis
8. Recommendation report
9. Equipment evaluation
10. Lab report
11. Trip report
12. Feasibility study
13. Proposal
14. Progress/report
15. Formal report
16. Job letter and résumé

# ABC Format 1: Positive Letter

## Abstract
- Bridge between this letter and last communication with reader
- Clear statement of good news you have to report

## Body
- Supporting data for main point mentioned in abstract
- Clarification of any questions reader may have
- Qualification, if any, of the good news

## Conclusion
- Statement of eagerness to continue relationship, complete project, etc.
- Clear statement, if appropriate, of what step should come next

### Helpful Hints

In the "bridge" (see Abstract), refer to your last contact with the reader or to the situation that prompted the letter (for example, "Thank you for your letter asking for a sample of our new Glide-Way bearings"). The good news comes immediately after the bridge—and sometimes even before it (for example, "Yes, we'll be glad to send you a free sample immediately"). In other words, good news always comes early in the letter. Any delay can cause confusion about the letter's purpose and can make the reader think, wrongly, that bad news is ahead.

**Martin & Koffman**

200 Fourth Avenue NW
Calgary AB T2N 0N3
(403) 555-7524

July 23, 2003

The Reverend Mr. John C. Davidson
Maxwell Street Church
Regina SK S3Y 4P1

Dear Reverend Davidson:

Thanks for your letter asking to reschedule the church project from mid-August to another, more convenient time. Yes, we'll be able to do the project on one of two possible dates in September, as explained below.

As you know, M&K originally planned to fit your foundation investigation between two other projects planned for the Regina area. In making every effort to lessen church costs, we would be saving money by having a crew already on site in your area—rather than having to charge you mobilization costs to and from Regina.

As it happens, we have just agreed to perform another large project in the Regina area beginning on September 18. We would be glad to schedule your project either before or after that job. Specifically, we could be at the church site for our one-day field investigation on either September 17 or September 25, whatever date you prefer.

Please call me by September 2 to let me know your scheduling preference for the project. In the meantime, have a productive and enjoyable conference at the church next month.

Sincerely,

*Nancy Wurcinski*

Nancy Wurcinski, P.E.
Project Manager

NW/mh
File #34678

**EXAMPLE 1**
Positive letter

Source: *Technical Writing: A Practical Approach*, 3rd Canadian Edition (p. 214) by W.S. Pfeiffer and J. Boogerd, 2004. Reprinted with permission by Pearson Education Canada Inc.

# ABC Format 2: Negative Letter

## Abstract

- Bridge between your letter and previous communication
- General statement of purpose or appreciation—in an effort to find common bond or area of agreement

## Body

- Strong emphasis on what can be done, when possible
- Buffered (yet clear) statement of what cannot be done, with reasons
- Facts that support your views

## Conclusion

- Closing remarks that express interest in continued association
- Statement, if appropriate, of what will happen next

### *Helpful Hints*

In negative letters, buffer the bad news but still be clear. Use the abstract to convey information that will help preserve goodwill and your relationship with the reader. Then use the body of the letter to state what can—and what cannot—be done. This approach assumes you want to retain your relationship with the reader and avoid "burning bridges." In the few cases where the relationship with the reader is gone—such as a request for payment that has been repeatedly ignored—a more direct approach may be necessary.

200 Fourth Avenue NW
Calgary AB T2N 0N3
(403) 555-7524

July 23, 2003

The Reverend Mr. John C. Davidson
Maxwell Street Church
Regina SK S3Y 4P1

Dear Reverend Davidson:

Thanks for your letter asking to reschedule the foundation project at your church from mid-August to late August, because of the regional conference. I am sure you are proud that Maxwell was chosen as the conference site.

One reason for our original schedule, as you may recall, was to save the travel costs for a project crew going back and forth between Calgary and Regina. Because M&K has several other jobs in the area, we had planned not to charge you for travel.

We can reschedule the project, as you request, to a more convenient date in late August, but the change will increase project costs from $1,500 to $2,400 to cover travel. At this point, we just don't have any other projects scheduled in your area in late August that would help defray the additional expenses. Given our low profit margin on such jobs, that additional $900 would make the difference between our firm making or losing money on the foundation investigation at your church.

I'll call you next week, Reverend Davidson, to select a new date that would be most suitable. M&K welcomes its association with the Maxwell Street Church and looks forward to a successful project in late August.

Sincerely,

*Nancy Wurcinski*

Nancy Wurcinski, P.E.
Project Manager

NW/mh
File #34678

## EXAMPLE 2
Negative letter

Source: *Technical Writing: A Practical Approach,* 3rd Canadian Edition (p. 215) by W.S. Pfeiffer and J. Boogerd, 2004. Reprinted with permission by Pearson Education Canada Inc.

# ABC Format 3: Neutral Letter

## Abstract

- Bridge or transition between letter and previous communication
- Exact purpose of letter (request, invitation, etc.)

## Body

- Details that support purpose statement—for example,
  —Description of item(s) requested
  —Requirements related to the invitation
  —Description of item(s) sent

## Conclusion

- Statement of appreciation
- Description of actions that should occur next

### Helpful Hints

Neutral letters must be absolutely clear about your inquiry or response. As in positive letters, make your point early so that there is no confusion about the message. Your first paragraph can include a bridge or transition sentence (for example, "Yesterday I called your warehouse to find out what calculators you have in stock"). It can be followed by a direct reference to the request (for example, "Using information provided by your staff, I want to order the nine calculators listed below").

Dawson
College

January 4, 2004

Ms. Angela Koffman, Manager
Martin & Koffman
2218 Rue Décarie
Montréal PQ H4T 1P9

Dear Ms. Koffman:

Martin & Koffman has hired eight graduates of Dawson College since 1998.
To help continue that tradition, we would like to invite you to the college's
first Career Fair, to be held February 21, 2004, from 8 a.m. until noon.

Sponsored by the Student Government Association, the Career Fair
gives students the opportunity to get to know more about a number of
potential employers. We give special attention to organizations, like
M&K, that have already had success in hiring Dawson College
graduates. Indeed, we have already had a number of inquiries about
whether your firm will be represented at the fair.

Participating in the Career Fair is simple. We will provide you with a
booth where one or two M&K representatives can talk with students who
come by to ask about your firm's career opportunities. Feel free to bring
along whatever brochures or other written information that would help
our students learn more about M&K's products and services.

I will call you next week, Ms. Koffman, to give more details about the
fair and offer a specific booth location. We at Dawson College look
forward to building on our already strong association with M&K.

Sincerely,

*Faron G. Abdulla*

14 Chemin Parizeau
Montréal PQ
H1R 9B0
(514) 555-0272

Faron G. Abdullah, President
Student Government Association

Copy: Gene Abrams, Placement Director

**EXAMPLE 3**
Neutral letter
Source: *Technical Writing: A Practical Approach,* 3rd Canadian Edition (p. 216) by W.S. Pfeiffer
and J. Boogerd, 2004. Reprinted with permission by Pearson Education Canada Inc.

# ABC Format 4: Sales Letter

## Abstract

■ Choose one or two of the following strategies for capturing attention:
—Cite a surprising fact
—Announce a new product or service
—Ask a question
—Show understanding of client's problem
—Show potential for solving client's problem
—Summarize results of a meeting
—Answer a question reader previously asked

## Body

■ Choose one or two of the following strategies for convincing the reader:
—Stress one main problem reader has concern about
—Stress one main selling point of your solution
—Emphasize what is unique about your solution
—Focus on value and quality, rather than price
—Put details in enclosures
—Briefly explain the value of any enclosures

## Conclusion

■ Keep control of the next step by doing the following:
—Leave the reader with one crucial point to remember
—Offer to call (first choice) or ask reader to call (last choice)

### Helpful Hints

The keywords above are *capture, convince,* and *control*—the "3Cs." Capture the readers' attention at the beginning, convince their minds in the middle, and control the next step at the end. Sales letters work together with personal contacts to build continuing relationships with customers.

Martin & Koffman

2218 Rue Décarie
Montréal PQ H4T 1P9

August 21, 2003

Mr. James Swartz, Safety Director
Jessup County School System
1111 Clay Street
Smiley, MO 64607

NEW ASBESTOS-ABATEMENT SERVICE NOW AVAILABLE

We enjoyed working with you last year, James, to update your entire fire alarm system. Given the current concern in the country about another safety issue, asbestos, we wanted you to know that our staff now does abatement work.

As you know, many of the state's school systems were constructed during years when asbestos was used as a primary insulator. No one knew then, of course, that the material can cause illness and even premature death for those who work in buildings where asbestos was used in construction. Now we know that just a small portion of asbestos produces a major health hazard.

Fortunately, there's a way to tell whether you have a problem: the asbestos survey. This procedure, done by our certified asbestos-abatement professionals, results in a report that tells whether or not your buildings are affected. And if we find asbestos, we can remove it for you.

Jessup showed real foresight in modernizing its alarm system last year, James. Your desire for a thorough job on that project was matched, as you know, by the approach we take to our business. Now we'd like to help give you the peace of mind that will come from knowing that either (1) there is no asbestos problem in your 35 structures or (2) you have removed the material.

The enclosed brochure outlines our asbestos services. I'll call you in a few days to see whether McDuff can help you out.

*Barbara Canzi*

Barbara H. Canzi
Certified Industrial Hygienist

BHC/sg

## EXAMPLE 4
Sales letter

Source: *Technical Writing: A Practical Approach,* 3rd Canadian Edition (p. 218) by W.S. Pfeiffer and J. Boogerd, 2004. Reprinted with permission by Pearson Education Canada Inc.

# ABC Format 5: Memorandum

## Abstract

- Clear statement of memo's purpose
- Outline of main parts of memo

## Body

- Absolute clarity about what memo has to do with reader
- Tactful presentation of any negative news
- Supporting points, with strong points at the beginning or end
- Frequent use of short paragraphs or lists
- Reference to attachments, when much detail is required

## Conclusion

- Clear statement of what step should occur next
- An effort to retain goodwill and cooperation of readers

### *Helpful Hints*

We spend more time reading and writing memos (including e-mail) than we want to admit. The main rule is to be clear, brief, and tactful. Because many activities are competing for your readers' time, memos should be written so that they can be understood immediately. Use headings and lists. Also, put the main point at the beginning, with a brief buffer if you are delivering bad news.

Martin & Koffman

## MEMORANDUM

DATE:       December 4, 2003
TO:         Technical Staff
FROM:       Ralph Simmons, Technical Manager RS
SUBJECT:    New Employees to Help with Technical Editing

Last week we hired an editor to help you produce top-quality reports, proposals, and other documents. This memorandum gives you some background on this change, highlights the credentials of our new editor, and explains what the change will mean to you.

**BACKGROUND**

At September's staff meeting, many technical staff members noted the excessive time spent editing and proofreading. For example, some of you said that this final stage of writing takes from 15–30 percent of the billable time on an average report. Most important, editing often ends up being done by project managers—the employees with the highest billable time.

Despite these editing efforts, many errors still show up in documents that go out the door. Last month I asked a committee of the Society of Technical Writers to review documents produced at Martin & Koffman. Their evaluation report reveals serious problems with our editing process. Given the importance of our documentation—it is the product delivered to our clients—I decided to seek a solution.

**SOLUTION: IN-HOUSE EDITOR**

To come to grips with this editing problem, the office just hired Ron Polus, an experienced technical editor. He'll start work January 3. For the last six years, Ron has worked as an editor at Jones Technical Services, a Toronto firm that does work similar to ours. Before that he completed a master's degree in technical writing at Sage University in Buffalo.

At next week's staff meeting, we'll discuss the best way to use Ron's skills to help us out. For now, he will be getting to know our work by reviewing recent reports and proposals. Also, the attached list of possible activities can serve as a springboard for our discussion.

**CONCLUSION**

By working together with Ron, we'll be able to improve the editorial quality of our documents, free up more of your time for technical tasks, and save the client and ourselves some money.

I look forward to meeting with you next week to discuss the best use of Ron's services.

Enclosure
Copy: Ron Polus

## EXAMPLE 5
Memorandum

Source: *Technical Writing: A Practical Approach*, 3rd Canadian Edition (p. 2186) by W.S. Pfeiffer and J. Boogerd, 2004. Reprinted with permission by Pearson Education Canada Inc.

# ABC Format 6: Instructions

## Abstract

- Clear purpose statement for instructions
- Summary of main steps
- List of materials or equipment needed (or reference to list or graphic)

## Body

- Helpful pointers or definitions
- Well-placed references to (1) Cautions (possibility of damage to things), (2) Warnings (possibility of injury), and (3) Dangers (probability of injury or death)
- Numbered steps
  —Steps grouped under main tasks, not presented in one "laundry list"
  —Limit of one action in each step
  —Use of verbs rather than nouns ("Check the meter reading")
- Separation of essential information (in steps) from helpful information (in "Notes" and "Results")

## Conclusion

- Statement, or restatement, about importance of procedure

### Helpful Hints

Instructions can be either freestanding documents or part of another document. In either case, the most common error is to make them too complicated for the audience. Carefully consider the technical level of your readers. Use white space, graphics, and other design elements to make the instructions appealing. Most important, be sure to include Caution, Warning, and Danger references *before* the steps to which they apply.

Martin & Koffman

MEMORANDUM

DATE:       June 5, 2003
TO:         All Employees
FROM:       Your Name
SUBJECT:    Basic Instructions for Viewing Your Calendar

Last month, you attended a brief seminar on the features of the new electronic calendar. We have just learned that the system will be installed on June 18. This memo provides some basic instructions for viewing your appointments on this system. Soon you will receive another set of instructions for entering your appointments.

NOTE: In these instructions, the messages or prompts on your terminal screen appear in *italics*. Any key you push or response you type is shown in **bold** print.

1. Double click on the calendar or icon on your desktop.
   NOTE: The technician will have placed one there when installing the software.

2. Type in your username when the system requests it.
   Example: *username:***EvanKinney**

3. Enter the temporary password provided to you.
   NOTE: Your temporary password will be the same as your username.
   Example: *password:* **EvanKinney**
   RESULT: After the system has verified your password, it will prompt you to

4. Enter your new password.
   NOTE: We recommend a password that does not describe a personal preference or characteristic since those are prone to hacking.

5. Confirm your choice by entering the password again.

6. Click on the button marked *AGENDA*.
   NOTE: The day's appointments entered for or by you will appear on the screen.

As noted earlier, the system will be installed on June 18. Feel free to call me if you have any questions about the installation or the instructions for viewing your calendar.

## EXAMPLE 6
Instructions

Source: *Technical Writing: A Practical Approach,* 3rd Canadian Edition (p. 167) by W.S. Pfeiffer and J. Boogerd, 2004. Reprinted with permission by Pearson Education Canada Inc.

# ABC Format 7: Problem Analysis

## Abstract

- Purpose of report
- Capsule summary of problems covered in report discussion

## Body

- Background on source of problems
- Well-organized description of problems observed
- Data that support your observations
- Consequences of the problems

## Conclusion

- Brief restatement of main problems (unless report is so short that restatement would be repetitious)
- Degree of urgency required in handling problems
- Suggested next step

### Helpful Hints

Problem analyses must provide an *objective* presentation of information, so that the readers (who are often decision makers) can decide upon the next step. Any opinions set forth must be well supported by facts.

### MEMORANDUM

DATE: October 15, 2003
TO: Jan Stillwright, Vice President of Research and Training
FROM: Harold Marshal, Technical Supervisor *HM*
SUBJECT: Boat Problems during Summer Season

### INTRODUCTORY SUMMARY

We have just completed a one-month project in the Pacific Ocean aboard the leased ship, *Seeker II.* All work went just about as planned, with very few delays caused by weather or equipment failure.

However, there were some boat problems that need to be solved before we lease *Seeker II* again this season. This report highlights the problems so that they can be brought to the owner's attention. My comments focus on four areas of the boat: drill rig, engineering lab, main engine, and crew quarters.

### DRILL RIG

Thus far the rig has operated without incident. Yet on one occasion, I noticed that the elevator for lifting pipe up the derrick swung too close to the derrick itself. A quick gust of wind or a sudden increase in sea height caused these shifts. If the elevator were to hit the derrick, causing the elevator door to open, pipe sections might fall to the deck below.

I believe the whole rig assembly must be checked by someone knowledgeable about its design. Before we put workers near that rig again, we need to know that their safety would not be jeopardized by the possibility of falling pipe.

### ENGINEERING LAB

Quite frankly, it is a tribute to our technicians that they were able to complete all lab tests with *Seeker II*'s limited facilities. Several weeks into the voyage, four main problems became apparent:

1. Ceiling leaks
2. Poor water pressure in the cleanup sink
3. Leaks around the window near the electronics corner
4. Two broken outlet plugs

Although we were able to devise a solution to the window leaks, the other problems stayed with us for the entire trip.

---

**EXAMPLE 7 (pp. 87–88)** *continues*
Problem analysis

Source: *Technical Writing: A Practical Approach,* 3rd Canadian Edition (pp. 249–250) by W.S. Pfeiffer and J. Boogerd, 2004. Reprinted with permission by Pearson Education Canada Inc.

**MAIN ENGINE**

On this trip, we had three valve failures on three different cylinder heads. From our experience on other ships, it is very unusual to have one valve fail, let alone three. Fortunately for us, these failures occurred between projects, so we did not lose time on a job. And fortunately for the owner, the broken valve parts did not destroy the engine's expensive turbocharger.

Only an expert will be able to tell whether these engine problems were flukes or if the entire motor needs to be rebuilt. In my opinion, the most prudent course of action is to have the engine checked over carefully before the next voyage.

**CREW QUARTERS**

When 15 men live in one room for three months, it is important that basic facilities work. On *Seeker II* we experienced problems with the bedroom, bathroom, and laundry room that caused some tension.

**Bedroom**

Three of the top bunks had such poor springs that the occupants sank 15 to 30 cm. toward the bottom bunks. More important, five of the bunks are not structurally sound enough to keep from swaying in medium to high seas. Finally, most of the locker handles are either broken or about to break.

**Bathroom**

Poor pressure in three of the commodes made them almost unusable during the last two weeks. Our amateur repairs did not solve the problem, so I think the plumbing leading to the holding tank might be defective.

**Laundry Room**

We discovered early that the filtering system could not screen the large amount of rust in the old 49,460 L tank. Consequently, undergarments and other white clothes turned a yellow-red colour and were ruined.

**CONCLUSION**

As noted at the outset, none of these problems kept us from accomplishing the major goals of this voyage. But they did make the trip much more uncomfortable than it had to be. Moreover, in the case of the rig and engine problems, we were fortunate that injuries and downtime did not occur.

I strongly urge that the owner be asked to correct these deficiencies before we consider using *Seeker II* for additional projects this season.

**EXAMPLE 7** *(continued)*

# ABC Format 8: Recommendation Report

## Abstract

- Purpose of report
- Brief reference to problem to which recommendations respond
- Capsule summary of recommendations covered in report

## Body

- Details about problem
- Well-organized description of recommendations
- Data that support recommendations (with reference to attachments)
- Main benefits of recommendations
- Any possible drawbacks

## Conclusion

- Brief restatement of main recommendations
- Main benefit of recommended change
- Your offer to help with next step

### Helpful Hints

Recommendation reports must be more persuasive than reports like problem analyses. Yet any recommendations in your report must be well supported by facts and analysis. You want readers to see your recommendations as ideas that flow naturally and inevitably from facts in the report.

Martin & Koffman

200 Fourth Ave. NW
Calgary AB T2N 0N3
(403) 555-7524

April 22, 2003


Shearwater Oil Inc.
12 Rankin St.
Edmonton AB T3L 2J6

**ATTENTION:** Mr. James Smith, Engineering Manager

**NOTRE DAME BAY STUDY**
**BLOCK 15, AREA 43-B**
**OFFSHORE NEWFOUNDLAND**

**INTRODUCTORY SUMMARY**

You recently asked our firm to complete a preliminary soils investigation at an offshore rig site. This report presents the tentative results of our study, including major conclusions and recommendations. A longer, formal report will follow at the end of the project.

On the basis of what we have learned so far, it is our opinion that you can safely place an oil platform at the Notre Dame Bay site. To limit the chance of a rig leg punching into the seafloor, however, we suggest you follow the recommendations in this report.

**WORK AT THE PROJECT SITE**

On April 16 and 17, 2003, M&K's engineers and technicians worked at the Block 15 site in the Notre Dame Bay region. Using M&K's leased drill ship, *Seeker II*, as a base of operations, our crew performed these main tasks:

- Seismic survey of the project study area, and
- Two soil borings of 12 m each.

Both seismic data and soil samples were brought to our Calgary office the next day for laboratory analysis.

**LABORATORY ANALYSIS**

On April 18 and 19, our lab staff examined the soil samples, completed bearing capacity tests, and evaluated seismic data. Here are the results of that analysis.

**Soil Layers**

Our initial evaluation of the soil samples reveals a 2–3 m layer of weak clay starting a few metres below the seafloor. Other than that layer, the composition of the soils seems fairly typical of other sites nearby.

**EXAMPLE 8 (pp. 92–93)**
Recommendation report
Source: *Technical Writing: A Practical Approach*, 3rd Canadian Edition (pp. 245–246) by W.S. Pfeiffer and J. Boogerd, 2004. Reprinted with permission by Pearson Education Canada Inc.

**Bearing Capacity**

We used the most reliable procedure available, the XYZ method, to determine the soil's bearing capacity (that is, its ability to withstand the weight of a loaded oil rig). That method required that we apply the following formula:

| | | |
|---|---|---|
| Q | = | cNv + tY, where |
| Q | = | ultimate bearing capacity |
| c | = | average cohesive shear strength |
| Nv | = | the dimensionless bearing capacity factor |
| t | = | footing displacement |
| Y | = | weight of the soil unit |

The final bearing capacity figure will be submitted in the final report, after we repeat the tests.

**Seafloor Surface**

By pulling our underwater seismometer back and forth across the project site, we developed a seismic "map" of the seafloor surface. That map seems typical of the flat floor expected in that area of the gulf. The only exception is the presence of what appears to be a small sunken boat. This wreck, however, is not in the immediate area of the proposed platform site.

**CONCLUSIONS AND RECOMMENDATIONS**

Based on our analysis, we conclude that there is only a slight risk of instability at the site. Though unlikely, it is possible that a rig leg could punch through the seafloor, either during or after loading. We base this opinion on (1) the existence of the weak clay layer, noted earlier, and (2) the marginal bearing capacity.

Nevertheless, we believe you can still place your platform if you follow careful rig-loading procedures. Specifically, take these precautions to reduce your risk:

1. Load the rig in 10-tonne increments, waiting one hour between loadings.
2. Allow the rig to stand 24 hours after the loading and before placement of workers on board.
3. Have a soils specialist observe the entire loading process, to assist with any emergency decisions if problems arise.

As noted at the outset, these conclusions and recommendations are based on preliminary data and analysis. We will complete our final study in three weeks and submit a formal report shortly thereafter.

M&K enjoyed working for Shearwater Oil at its offshore Newfoundland lease holdings. I will phone you this week to see if you have any questions about our study. If you need information before then, please give me a call.

Sincerely,

*Bartley Dowdell*

Bartley Dowdell, Project Manager
Martin & Koffman

hg

**EXAMPLE 8** *(continued)*

# ABC Format 9: Equipment Evaluation

## Abstract

- Purpose of report
- Capsule summary of what report says about the equipment

## Body

- Thorough description of equipment being evaluated
- Well-organized critique, either analyzing the parts of one piece of equipment or contrasting several pieces of similar equipment
- Additional supporting data, with reference to attachments

## Conclusion

- Brief restatement of major findings, conclusions, or recommendations

### Helpful Hints

Equipment evaluations give objective critiques about how equipment has functioned. Possible topics include machinery, tools, vehicles, software, and office supplies. Like a problem analysis, the equipment evaluation may focus on problems. Or, like a recommendation report, it may suggest a change. In any case, it must provide well-documented observations of the manner in which equipment has performed.

**MEMORANDUM**

DATE:       July 26, 2003
TO:         Marta Cesta, Office Manager
FROM:       Hank Worley, Assistant Manager  *HW*
SUBJECT:    Evaluation of Best Choice Software

**INTRODUCTORY SUMMARY**

You asked us to evaluate Best Choice Software last month in order to determine whether it would be worth purchasing. Having used the package, I find it meets our performance specifications. I recommend that we use it in our office and that we recommend it to our clients.

**HOW BEST CHOICE HAS HELPED US**

Best Choice provides five primary features: word processing, file management, spreadsheet, graphics, and a user's guide. Here is my critique of all five.

**Word Processing**

The system contains an excellent word-processing package that the engineers as well as the secretaries have been able to learn easily. This package can handle both our routine correspondence and the lengthy reports that our group generates. Of particular help are the system's Canadian, American, and British dictionaries, which can be updated at any time. The spelling correction feature has already saved much effort that was previously devoted to mechanical editing.

**File Management**

The file manager function allows the user to enter information and then to manipulate it quickly. During one three-day site visit, for example, a field engineer recorded a series of problems observed in the field. Then she rearranged the data to highlight specific points I asked her to study, such as I-beam welds and concrete cracks.

**Spreadsheet**

Like the system's word-processing package, the spreadsheet is efficient and quickly learned. Because Best Choice is a multipurpose software package, spreadsheet data can be incorporated into letter or report format. In other words, spreadsheet information can be merged with our document format to create a final draft for submission to clients or supervisors, with a real savings in time. For example, the memo I sent you last week on budget projections for field equipment took me only an hour to complete; last quarter, the identical project took four hours.

**EXAMPLE 9 (pp. 93–94)**
Equipment evaluation

Source: *Technical Writing: A Practical Approach,* 3rd Canadian Edition (pp. 247–248) by W.S. Pfeiffer and J. Boogerd, 2004. Reprinted with permission by Pearson Education Canada Inc.

Marta Cesta
July 26, 2003
Page 2

**Graphics**

The graphics package permits visuals to be drawn from the data contained in the spreadsheet. For example, a pie chart that shows the breakdown of a project budget can be created easily by merging spreadsheet data with the graphics software. With visuals becoming such an important part of reports, we have used this feature of Best Choice quite frequently.

**User's Guide**

Eight employees in my group have now used the Best Choice user's guide. All have found it well laid out and thorough. Perhaps the best indication of this fact is that in 30 days of daily use, we have placed only three calls to the Best Choice customer-service number.

**CONCLUSION**

Best Choice seems to contain just the right combination of tools to help us do our job, both in the field and in the office. These are the system's main benefits:

- Versatility—it has diverse functions
- Simplicity—it is easy to master

The people in our group have been very pleased with the package during this 30-day trial. If you like, we would be glad to evaluate Best Choice for a longer period.

**EXAMPLE 9** *(continued)*

# ABC Format 10: Lab Report

## Abstract

- Purpose of report
- Capsule summary of results

## Body

- Purpose or hypothesis of lab work
- Equipment needed
- Procedures or methods used in the lab test
- Unusual problems or occurrences
- Results of the test with reference to your expectations (results may appear in conclusion, instead)

## Conclusion

- Restatement of main results
- Implications of lab test for further work

### Helpful Hints

Like procedures, lab reports may stand on their own or be part of a larger report that uses lab work for supporting detail. Lab reports usually include topics such as procedures, equipment, problems, results, and implications.

Martin & Koffman

200 Fourth Ave. NW
Calgary AB T2N 0N3
(403) 555-7524

December 12, 2003

Mr. Andrew Hawkes
Monson Coal Company
2139 Lasiter Dr.
Baltimore, MD 21222

**LABORATORY REPORT**
**BOREHOLE FOSSIL SAMPLES**
**BRAINTREE CREEK SITE, WEST VIRGINIA**

**INTRODUCTORY SUMMARY**

Last week you sent us six fossilized samples from the Braintree Creek site. Having analyzed the samples in our lab, we believe they suggest the presence of coal-bearing rock. As you requested, this report will give a summary of the materials and procedures we used in this project, along with any problems we had.

As you know, our methodology in this kind of job is to identify microfossils in the samples, estimate the age of the rock by when the microfossils existed, and then make assumptions about whether the surrounding rock might contain coal.

**LAB MATERIALS**

Our lab analysis relies on only one piece of specialized equipment: a Piketon electron microscope. Besides the Piketon, we use a simple 400-power manual microscope. Other equipment is similar to that included in any basic geology lab, such as filtering screens and burners.

**LAB PROCEDURE**

Once we receive a sample, we first try to identify the exact kinds of microfossils that the rocks contain. Our specific lab procedure for your samples consisted of these two steps:

**Step 1**

We used a 400-power microscope to visually classify the microfossils that were present. Upon inspection of the samples, we concluded that there were two main types of microfossils: nannoplankton and foraminifera.

**EXAMPLE 10 (pp. 96–97)**

Lab report

Source: *Technical Writing: A Practical Approach,* 3rd Canadian Edition (pp. 254–255) by W.S. Pfeiffer and J. Boogerd, 2004. Reprinted with permission by Pearson Education Canada Inc.

**Step 2**

Next, we had to extract the microfossils from the core samples you provided. We used two different techniques:

**Nannoplankton Extraction Technique**

a. Selected a pebble-size piece of the sample
b. Thoroughly crushed the piece under water
c. Used a dropper to remove some of the material that floats to the surface (it contains the nannoplankton)
d. Dried the nannoplankton-water combination
e. Placed the nannoplankton on a slide

**Foraminifera Extraction Technique**

a. Boiled a small portion of the sample
b. Used a microscreen to remove clay and other unwanted material
c. Dried remaining material (foraminifera)
d. Placed foraminifera on slide

**PROBLEMS ENCOUNTERED**

The entire lab procedure went as planned. The only problem was minor and occurred when we removed one of the samples from the container in which it was shipped. As the bag was taken from the shipping box, it broke open. The sample shattered when it fell onto the lab table. Fortunately, we had an extra sample from the same location.

**CONCLUSION**

Judging by the types of fossils present in the sample, they come from rock of an age that might contain coal. This conclusion is based on limited testing, so we suggest you test more samples at the site. We would be glad to help you with this additional sampling and testing.

I will call you this week to discuss our study and any possible follow-up you may wish us to do.

Sincerely,

*Joanne Rappaport*

Joanne Rappaport
Senior Geologist

**EXAMPLE 10** *(continued)*

# ABC Format 11: Trip Report

## Abstract

- Destination, dates, and purpose of trip
- Brief overview of results of trip
- Main sections of report

## Body

- Major accomplishments, grouped by task
- Any conclusions that flow from your work
- Any recommendations you developed
- Administrative details, such as trip expenses

## Conclusion

- Wrap-up that refers to overall usefulness of the trip
- Follow-up activities that may be required

### *Helpful Hints*

Trip reports can be so routine at some organizations that brief forms are used. In other organizations they are anything but routine. Assume the latter unless you know otherwise. Your organization has invested in your trip and expects you to be able to describe your accomplishments.

**MEMORANDUM**

DATE:       July 15, 2003
TO:         Susan Newton, Manager of Marketing
FROM:       Stone Prentice, Marketing Specialist *SP*
SUBJECT:    Report on Trip to Seattle

Last Friday I visited Seattle to explore several marketing opportunities for our firm. Having met with two potential clients, I believe we should strongly consider entering the Seattle market. This report highlights the results of my trip and proposes some follow-up activities for your review.

**MEETINGS WITH POTENTIAL CLIENTS**
In Seattle I met with officials from the two companies you asked me to contact. Both expressed interest in M&K's, as noted below.

**Meeting with Josh McDonald, Pacific Retro Services**
I spent the morning of July 11 with Mr. McDonald, reviewing his firm's projects for the next two years. He wants us to submit proposals for three upcoming projects to improve the indoor air quality (IAQ) of several downtown buildings. Further, he noted he has heard good comments about our patented IAQ equipment.

**Meeting with Maureen Hemphill, the Builders Group**
In the afternoon of July 11, I met with Ms. Hemphill at one of her firm's largest current projects, the 110 Jackson Building. She noted that her executive staff has been unhappy with delays in construction; it would like to consider hiring a firm like ours to manage construction for future projects. In fact, the Builders Group will issue two large requests for proposals before September.

**PROPOSED PLAN OF ACTION**
Pacific Retro Services and the Builders Group may offer us a lucrative Seattle market for our services. I suggest a threefold plan of action:

1. Submit proposals for all future projects for which we are qualified
2. Study the feasibility of starting a small branch in Seattle
3. Conduct future marketing trips in Seattle

**CLOSING**
I would be glad to help with the follow-up activities listed above. Seattle offers us a good opportunity to expand our work and provide a useful service.

**EXAMPLE 11**
Trip report

# ABC Format 12: Feasibility Study

## Abstract

- Brief statement about who authorized study and for what purpose
- Brief statement of overall recommendation
- Reference to main parts of report

## Body

- Description of methods used in study
- Description of evaluation criteria (cost, schedule, quality, etc.)
- Analysis of item or items, according to the evaluation criteria
- Detailed information about advantages and disadvantages of adopting the change
- Other alternatives to consider, if any

## Conclusion

- Major conclusions and recommendations resulting from study
- Follow-up tasks that may be needed to acquire additional data

### *Helpful Hints*

Unlike proposals, feasibility studies are always requested by the readers. They are needed to determine the practicality—that is, feasibility—of a proposed policy, product, or service. Readers need information from the study to make decisions.

MEMORANDUM

DATE:      July 22, 2003
TO:        Nizar Bhindi
FROM:      Mike Tran  *MT*
SUBJECT:   Replacement of In-House File Server

**INTRODUCTORY SUMMARY**

The purpose of this feasibility study is to determine if the NTR PC905 would make a practical replacement for our in-house file server. As we agreed in our weekly staff meeting, our current file-serving computer is damaged beyond repair and must be replaced by the end of the week. This study shows that the NTR PC905 is a suitable replacement that we can purchase within our budget and install by Friday afternoon.

**FEASIBILITY CRITERIA**

There are three major criteria that I addressed. First, the computer we buy must be able to perform the tasks of a file-serving computer on our in-house network. Second, it must be priced within our $4,000 budget for the project. Third, it must be delivered and installed by Friday afternoon.

**Performance**

As a file server, the computer we buy must be able to satisfy these criteria:

- Store all programs used by network computers
- Store the source code and customer-specific files for Xtracheck
- Provide fast transfer of files between computers while serving as host to the network
- Serve as the printing station for the network laser printer

The NTR PC905 comes with a 10.0 GB hard drive. This capacity will provide an adequate amount of storage for all programs that will reside on the file server. Our requirements are for 2 GB of storage for programs used by network computers and 2.5 GB of storage for source code and customer-specific programs. The 10.0 GB drive will leave us with 5.5 GB of storage for future growth and work space.

The PC905 can transfer files and execute programs across our network. It can perform these tasks at speeds up to five times faster than our current file server. Productivity should increase because the time spent waiting for transfer will decrease.

**EXAMPLE 12 (pp. 101–102)**
Feasibility study

Source: *Technical Writing: A Practical Approach*, 3rd Canadian Edition (pp. 365–366) by W.S. Pfeiffer and J. Boogerd, 2004. Reprinted with permission by Pearson Education Canada Inc.

The computer we choose as the file server must also serve as the printing station for our network laser printer. The PC905 is compatible with our Hewy Packer laser printer. It also has double the memory of our current server. As a result, it can store larger documents in memory and print them with greater speed.

**Budget**

The budget for the new file server is $4,000. The cost of the PC905 is as follows:

| | |
|---|---|
| PC905 with 10.0 GB Hard Drive | $2,910 |
| Keyboard | 112 |
| Monitor | 759 |
| Total | $3,781 |

No new network boards need to be purchased because we can use those that are in the current server. We also have all additional hardware and cables that will be required for installation. Thus the PC905 can be purchased for $200 under budget.

**Time Frame**

Our sales representative at NTR guarantees that we can have delivery of the system by Friday morning. Given this assurance, we can have the system in operation by Friday afternoon.

**Additional Benefits**

We are currently using NTR PCs at our customer sites. I am very familiar with the setup and installation of these machines. By purchasing a brand of computer currently in use, we will not have to worry about additional time spent learning new installation and operation procedures. In addition, we know that all our software is fully compatible with NTR products.

The warranty on the PC905 is for one year. After the warranty period, the equipment is covered by the service plan that we have for all our other computers and printers.

**CONCLUSION**

I recommend that we purchase the NTR PC905 as the replacement computer for our file server. It meets or exceeds all criteria for performance, price, and installation.

**EXAMPLE 12** *(continued)*

# ABC Format 13: Proposal

## Abstract

- Purpose of proposal
- Main need of the readers
- Main feature of what you are offering
- Main benefit to reader of the feature noted above
- Main sections to follow

## Body

- Problem or need and its significance
- Proposed solution or approach
- People to be used and their qualifications
- Schedule to be followed
- Cost of what is being proposed

## Conclusion

- Restatement of a main feature or benefit or both
- Clarification of your interest in the work
- Statement about what should happen next

### *Helpful Hints*

Long and short proposals cover the same basic topics—needs, features, and benefits. Yet long proposals respond to more complex projects and are presented as formal documents, much like formal reports (see ABC Format 15). Whether long or short, proposals can be either in-house documents or sales proposals directed to customers.

DATE:      October 4, 2003
TO:        Gerri le Bon
FROM:      Jeff Bilstrom  *JB*
SUBJECT:   Creation of Logo for Montrose Service Centre

Part of my job as director of public relations is to get the Montrose name firmly entrenched in the minds of Montréal Urban Community residents. Having recently reviewed the contacts we have with the public, I believe we are sending a confusing message about the many services we offer retired citizens in this area.

To remedy the problem, I propose we adopt a logo to serve as an umbrella for all services and agencies supported by the Montrose Service Centre. This proposal gives details about the problem and the proposal solution, including costs.

**The Problem**

The lack of a logo presents a number of problems related to marketing the centre's services and informing the public. Here are a few:

- The letterhead mentions the organization's name in small type, with none of the impact that an accompanying logo would have.
- The current brochure needs the flair that could be provided by a logo on the cover page, rather than just the page of text and headings that we now have.
- Our 14 vehicles are difficult to identify because there is only the lettered organization name on the sides without any readily identifiable graphic.
- The sign in front of our campus, a main piece of free advertising, could better spread the word about Montrose if it contained a catchy logo.
- Other signs around campus could display the logo, as a way of reinforcing our identity and labelling buildings.

It's clear that without a logo, the Montrose Service Centre misses an excellent opportunity to educate the public about its services.

**The Solution**

I believe a professionally designed logo could give the Montrose Service Centre a more distinct identity. Helping to tie together all branches of our operation, it would give the public an easy-to-recognize symbol. As a result, there would be a stronger awareness of the centre on the part of potential users and financial contributors.

**EXAMPLE 13 (pp. 104–105)**
Proposal
Source: *Technical Writing: A Practical Approach,* 3rd Canadian Edition (pp. 354–355) by W.S. Pfeiffer and J. Boogerd, 2004. Reprinted with permission by Pearson Education Canada Inc.

The new logo could be used immediately to:

- Design and print letterhead, envelopes, business cards, and a new brochure.
- Develop a decal for all company vehicles that would identify them as belonging to Montrose.
- Develop new signs for the entire campus, to include a new sign for the entrance to the campus, one sign at the entrance to the Blane Workshop, and one sign at the entrance to the Administration Building.

**Cost**

Developing a new logo can be quite expensive. However, I have been able to get the name of a well-respected graphic artist in Montréal who is willing to donate his services in the creation of a new logo. All that we must do is give him some general guidelines to follow and then choose among eight to ten rough sketches. Once a decision is made, the artist will provide a camera-ready copy of the new logo.

- Design charge                                       $0.00
- Charge for new letterhead, envelopes,
  business cards, and brochures
  (min. order)                                       545.65
- Decal for vehicles 14 @ $50.00 + 4%      728.00
- Signs for campus                                  415.28
                                                    ----------
  Total Cost                                      $1,688.93

**Conclusion**

As the retirement population of Montréal increases in the next few years, there will be a much greater need for the services of the Montrose Service Centre. Because of that need, it's in our best interests to keep this growing market informed about the organization.

I'll stop by later this week to discuss any questions you might have about this proposal.

**EXAMPLE 13** *(continued)*

# ABC Format 14: Progress Report

## Abstract

- Purpose of report
- Overview of project
- Survey of progress since last report

## Body

- Tasks completed since last report—organized by task or time or both
- Clear reference to dead ends that have taken time but yielded no results
- Explanation of delays or incomplete work
- Work remaining on project(s)—organized by task or time or both
- Reference to attachments that may contain more specific information

## Conclusion

- Brief restatement of work since last reporting period
- Expression of confidence, or concern, about overall work on project
- Indication of willingness to make adjustments the reader may suggest

### Helpful Hints

Progress reports are usually organized by task or by time. The reader, perhaps your supervisor or your customer, wants details about the status of a project. Whereas you should put forth the best case for the work you have completed, be certain not to overstate what you have done.

Martin & Koffman

## MEMORANDUM

DATE:     June 11, 2003
TO:       Jacques Martin, President, M&K
FROM:     Aziz Rashid *AR*
SUBJECT:  Progress Report on Training

### INTRODUCTORY SUMMARY

On May 21 you asked that I study ways our firm can improve training for technical employees in all domestic offices. We agreed that the project would take about six or seven weeks and involve three phases:

Phase 1: Make phone inquiries to competing firms
Phase 2: Send a survey to our technical people
Phase 3: Interview a cross-section of our technical employees

I have now completed Phase 1 and part of Phase 2. My observation thus far is that the project will offer many new directions to consider for our technical training program.

### WORK COMPLETED

In the first week of the project, I had extensive phone conversations with people at three competing firms about their training programs. Then in the second week, I wrote and sent out a training survey to all technical employees in M&K's offices.

#### Phone Interviews

I contacted three firms for whom we have done similar favours in the past: Simkins Consultants, Judd & Associates, and ABG Engineering. Here is a summary of my conversations:

1. Simkins Consultants
   Talked with Harry Rolak, training director, on May 23. Harry said that his firm has most success with internal training seminars. Each technical person completes several one- or two-day seminars every year. These courses are conducted by in-house experts or external consultants, depending on the specialty.

2. Judd & Associates
   Talked with Jan Tyler, manager of engineering, on May 24. Jan said that Judd, like Simkins, depends mostly on internal seminars. But Judd spreads these seminars over one or two weeks, rather than teaching intensive courses in one or two days. Judd also offers short "technical awareness" sessions at the lunch hour every two weeks. In-house technical experts give informal presentations on some aspect of their research or fieldwork.

## EXAMPLE 14 (pp. 107–108)
### Progress report

Source: *Technical Writing: A Practical Approach*, 3rd Canadian Edition (pp. 251–252) by W.S. Pfeiffer and J. Boogerd, 2004. Reprinted with permission by Pearson Education Canada Inc.

3. ABG Engineering
   Talked with Newt Mosely, personnel coordinator, on May 27. According to Newt, ABG's training program is much as it was two decades ago. Most technical people at high levels go to one seminar a year, usually sponsored by professional societies or local colleges. Other technical people get little training beyond what is provided on the job. In-house training has not worked well, mainly because of schedule conflicts with engineering jobs.

**Internal Survey**

After completing the phone interviews noted, I began the survey phase of the project. Last week, I finished writing the survey, had it reproduced, and sent it with cover memo to all technical employees in our offices. The deadline for returning it to me is June 17.

**WORK PLANNED**

With phone interviews finished and the survey mailed, I foresee the following schedule for completing the project:

| | |
|---|---|
| June 17: | Surveys returned |
| June 18–21: | Surveys evaluated |
| June 24–28: | Trips taken to all domestic offices to interview a cross-section of technical employees |
| July 3: | Submission of final project report to you |

**CONCLUSION**

My interviews with competitors gave me a good feel for what technical training might be appropriate for our staff. Now I am hoping for a high-percentage return on the internal survey. That phase will prepare a good foundation for my on-site interviews later this month. I believe this major corporate effort will upgrade our technical training considerably.

I would be glad to hear any suggestions you may have about my work on the rest of the project. For example, please call if you have any particular questions you want asked during the on-site interviews (ext. 348).

**EXAMPLE 14** *(continued)*

# ABC Format 15: Formal Report

## Abstract

- Cover/title page
- Letter or memo of transmittal
- Table of contents
- List of illustrations
- Executive summary
- Introduction

## Body

- Discussion sections
- [Appendices—appear after text but support body section]

## Conclusion

- Conclusions
- Recommendations

### *Helpful Hints*

The term "formal report" refers to documents of a certain length (at least 6 to 10 pages of text) and degree of formality (usually bound, with formal covers and graphics). They cover complex projects and can include one or more types of information noted in previous ABC models. One part of the formal report—the executive summary—is especially important to decision makers.

# PROJECT NO. 10525

# REPORT TO

# LUNDY CONSTRUCTION

# ON

# PROPOSED PUBLIC LIBRARY
# ORLEANS BRANCH
# GLOUCESTER, ONTARIO

Martin & Koffman
2218 Rue Décarie
Montréal, Québec
H1Q 2C1
Tel: (514) 555-6431
Fax: (514) 555-0825
August 19, 2004

**EXAMPLE 15 (pp. 110–130)**
Formal report
Source: *Technical Writing: A Practical Approach,* 3rd Canadian Edition (pp. 292–312) by W.S.
Pfeiffer and J. Boogerd, 2004. Reprinted with permission by Pearson Education Canada Inc.

## TABLE OF CONTENTS

**EXAMPLE 15** *(continued)*

**SUMMARY**

Soil conditions at the site of the proposed Gloucester Library were examined in order to determine how to guarantee the stability of the structure. The examination of the soil conditions at the site revealed that there is a stable crust on top of a soft layer of silty clay. The more solid layer at the top will, if not ruptured, support the building securely. Since footings have to be located in the lower (softer) layer, surcharge should be placed on the site in order to consolidate the silty clay prior to loading.

**EXAMPLE 15** *(continued)*

## 1.0 INTRODUCTION

This report presents the results of a geotechnical investigation carried out for the proposed City of Gloucester Public Library, Orleans Branch, located on the east side of Orleans Boulevard, south of Beausejour Street, in Barrington Park, Gloucester, Ontario. Authorization to carry out the work was received from Mr. Enzo DiChiara, P.Eng., of Lundy Construction Limited.

This report has been prepared specifically and solely for the above-noted project which is described herein. It contains all of our findings and includes geotechnical recommendations for the design and construction of the proposed library, parking area and access ways.

## 2.0 PROPOSED DEVELOPMENT

The site is located on the east side of Orleans Boulevard in Barrington Park, Gloucester, Ontario, as shown on Drawing 10525–1, Appendix 2. The layout of the proposed building and paved area is shown on Drawing 10525–2 in Appendix 2.

It is understood that the proposed building is to be a single-storey structure with no basement, with a plan area of 1,500 m$^2$. It is understood that the finished floor will be a slab-on-grade at an elevation near existing grades. The building is to be surrounded mainly by grassed areas with a parking area for approximately 100 vehicles to the northeast. An access road to the parking lot will be provided from Orleans Boulevard.

## 3.0 SCOPE OF WORK

The scope of work for this investigation is as follows:

- Conduct a geotechnical investigation (minimum three building and two parking lot boreholes).
- Carry out laboratory testing required to define the characteristics of the subsurface soils.
- Provide geotechnical recommendations for the design and construction of the proposed building, parking structure, and access road.

Environmental-related issues are outside the scope of work of this investigation.

## 4.0 METHODS OF INVESTIGATION

### 4.1 Field Investigation

Prior to the commencement of the investigation, the borehole locations were cleared of underground utilities by Martin & Koffman (M&K) personnel. The fieldwork for this investigation was carried out on August 11, 2004. A total of five boreholes, numbered BH 94–1 to 94–5, were put down using a track-mounted CME power

1

**EXAMPLE 15** *(continued)*

auger at the locations indicated on Drawing 10525–2 in Appendix 2. Three (3) boreholes were put down within the proposed building footprint and two (2) boreholes were put down within the area of the proposed paved parking lot.

The subsurface stratigraphy encountered in each borehole was recorded in the field by our personnel. Representative samples of each stratum encountered were collected by conducting Standard Penetration Tests. In-situ vane shear tests were carried out at close intervals to assess the undrained shear strength of cohesive soils. All samples were stored in moisture-proof bags and were returned to our laboratory for detailed classification and testing. All boreholes were backfilled and compacted with the augered material.

Standpipe piezometers were installed in Boreholes 94–1, 94–2 and 94–3 for groundwater level monitoring. Groundwater levels were recorded on the day of drilling as well as on August 17, 2004, to confirm static water levels.

### 4.2    Survey

Borehole locations were laid out in the field by M&K personnel relative to existing site features. Ground surface elevations at the borehole locations were determined with reference to an elevation of 86.64 m for a catch basin located on Orleans Boulevard, across from the existing fire hydrant adjacent to the site. This benchmark elevation was taken from a topographical plan prepared by Annis, O'Sullivan, Vollebekk Limited for Lundy Construction Limited.

### 4.3    Laboratory Testing

All samples returned to the laboratory were subjected to detailed visual classification by a geotechnical engineer. Selected samples were tested for moisture content.

Samples remaining after testing will be stored for a period of three months after issuance of this report. Samples will then be discarded unless we are otherwise directed.

### 5.0    RESULTS OF INVESTIGATION

### 5.1    Surface Conditions

It is understood that the site of the proposed library has not been previously developed, although it has been used as a municipal park. The ground surface is generally flat. Grass is present at ground surface across the site with a few trees.

### 5.2    Subsurface Profile

The subsurface conditions observed in the boreholes are presented in detail on the Borehole Records provided in Appendix 1. An explanation of the symbols and terms used to describe the Borehole Records is also provided.

In general, the observed stratigraphy consists of topsoil overlying fill, sand or silt with some clay over silty clay. Boreholes were terminated within the silty clay layer. The observed soil conditions are briefly summarized below.

2

**EXAMPLE 15** *(continued)*

### 5.2.1 Surficial Materials

A layer of topsoil 100 to 440 mm in thickness was encountered at the ground surface in all of the boreholes.

### 5.2.2 Fill

A layer of fill consisting of silty clay, trace gravel, trace sand, and trace asphalt was observed below the topsoil in Boreholes 94–4 and 94–5. The fill was found to range in thickness between 300 and 600 mm.

### 5.2.3 Sand

A layer of loose sand, trace silt was encountered below the fill in Borehole 94–5. The thickness of this layer was 600 mm.

### 5.2.4 Silt with Some Clay

A weathered layer of silt with some clay soil was encountered in Boreholes 94–1 and 94–2 beneath the topsoil. The unit was observed to range in thickness from 400 to 500 mm.

### 5.2.5 Silty Clay

Silty clay was encountered in all boreholes below the surficial materials. The silty clay layer can be subdivided into an upper, brown to grey, firm to stiff crust and underlying softer, grey materials.

The crust was consistently observed to extend to a depth of 2.9 m below existing grade in BH 94–1, 94–2, and 94–3. Boreholes 94–5 and 94–6 did not fully penetrate the crust. The moisture content of this layer ranged from 23 to 46% and averaged 38% for the five samples tested. In-situ shear vane values indicate the undrained shear strength of the crust in the areas tested ranges from 30 to 79 kPa, indicating a firm to stiff consistency. The remoulded strengths range from 5 to 24 kPa.

The deeper grey material is softer and has a higher moisture content than the overlying crust. The moisture content of the deeper grey silty clay ranged from 50 to 88% and averaged 73% in the samples tested. In-situ shear vane values indicate the undrained shear strength of the grey silty clay in the areas tested from 17 to 34 kPa, indicating a soft to firm consistency. The remoulded strengths were consistently under 5 kPa.

### 5.3 Groundwater

The groundwater table was not observed within the boreholes during drilling. Standpipe piezometers were installed in Boreholes 94–1, 94–2, and 94–3. Groundwater was observed in the standpipes at depths between 1.0 and 1.2 m on August 17, 2004.

Fluctuations in the groundwater level due to seasonal variations or in response to a particular precipitation event should be anticipated.

3

**EXAMPLE 15 *(continued)***

## 6.0   DISCUSSION AND RECOMMENDATIONS

### 6.1   General

The subsurface soils encountered at the site consist of fill, sand, or silt with clay overlying a stiff to firm silty clay crust overlying firm to soft silty clay. Based on the soil conditions determined and the expected loadings, it is anticipated that conventional spread footings founded on undisturbed silty clay could possibly be adequate in supporting the proposed structure. However, the presence of the soft, sensitive clays limits the size and type of structure that can be constructed at this site using conventional spread footings. Conventional spread footings may be used provided they are placed within the crust material and are limited in size to avoid overstressing the lower, weaker clay deposit. Furthermore, steps must be taken to ensure additional loads, such as those imposed by placement of additional fill, are limited to avoid long-term settlement problems. Recommendations for maximum footing pressures and footing size are provided in Section 6.3.

The following sections outline our recommendations for the design and construction of the proposed building, the parking lot pavement structure, and access road.

### 6.2   Site Grading and Preparation

The surficial vegetation, topsoil, fill, and other deleterious materials must be stripped from within the influence zone of the foundations for the building. The influence zone is defined by a line drawn at 1 horizontal to 1 vertical away and downward from the edge of the footings. Structural fill should be used to raise the grade to the underside of the footings as required.

Fill placement beneath or immediately adjacent to the building or paved areas should be limited to a maximum of 0.5 m above the original ground surface. This limitation was used in the calculation of bearing capacities in Section 6.3.

All surficial vegetation, topsoil, and rootmat should be removed from beneath the floor slab and paved areas. The exposed subgrade should be inspected and approved by a geotechnical engineer. Proof rolling using a large roller may be required to identify soft areas. All soft areas revealed under proof rolling must be removed and replaced with compacted fill. OPSS Select Subgrade Material may be used as fill below the subgrade line in paved areas.

Structural fill should consist of clean sand and gravel, such as OPSS Granular B, Type I. This material should be tested and approved by a geotechnical engineer prior to delivery to the site. Structural fill should be placed in lifts no thicker than 300 mm and compacted using suitable compaction equipment to at least 98% Standard Proctor maximum dry density.

The compaction requirement for Select Subgrade Material used as subgrade fill in paved areas should be at least 95% Standard Proctor maximum dry density.

The silty clay soils present at this site are generally suitable for reuse as grading fills only within landscaped areas.

4

**EXAMPLE 15** *(continued)*

Earth removal should be inspected by a geotechnical engineer to ensure that all unsuitable materials are removed prior to placement of structural fill. Inspection and testing services will also be required to ensure that all fill is placed and compacted to the required degree.

### 6.3 Spread Footings

Spread footings may be placed directly on undisturbed silty clay crust or placed on a pad of engineered fill placed on undisturbed silty clay crust. The following bearing capacities are recommended for the design of the structure:

| Bearing Elevation | Bearing Material | Factored capacity at ULS | Capacity at SLS Type II |
|---|---|---|---|
| 84.7 or higher | Silty Clay or Structural Fill | 100 kPa | 75 kPa |
| Below 84.7 | Grey Silty Clay | Not recommended | Not recommended |

It has been assumed that regrading of the site will be limited to 0.5 m of fill above present grades and that floor loads will not be greater than 10 kPa on average. The total and differential settlements associated with the recommended bearing capacity under these conditions will be less than 25 mm for strip footings as wide as 1 m and square footings as large as 1 m by 1 m in size, provided the footings are not placed deeper than the above recommended elevation.

All exterior footings and footings located within 1 m distance from the exterior walls will require a minimum soil cover of 1.5 m for protection against frost action. Footings in unheated areas or exterior footings for signs or canopies should be founded at least 1.8 m below exterior grade to protect against frost action. Where adequate soil cover cannot be accommodated, insulation may be considered as a means of ensuring sufficient frost protection. Design of the insulation should be reviewed by the geotechnical engineer.

The base of all footing excavations should be inspected by a geotechnical engineer prior to placing concrete to confirm the above design pressures and to ensure there is no disturbance. Any disturbed material identified during the inspection will need to be removed and wasted.

Where construction is undertaken during winter conditions, footing subgrades should be protected from freezing and foundation walls and columns should be protected against heave due to soil adfreeze. It is understood that the construction schedule may result in construction of the earthworks and foundations during the fall of 2004 with the building remaining incomplete and unheated through the winter. Insulation must be provided for the footings and foundation walls in this circumstance.

5

**EXAMPLE 15** *(continued)*

### 6.4    Floor Slab

A conventional slab-on-grade unit is suitable for use for the proposed building provided the site is prepared as outlined in Section 6.2. A layer of free-draining granular material should be placed immediately beneath the floor slab for levelling and support purposes. It is recommended that at least 200 mm of approved crushed stone be used, this material should be compacted to at least 98% Standard Proctor maximum dry density. Perimeter drains should be installed if the final grades around the building are higher than the underside of the slab.

The floor slab constructed as recommended above may be designed using a soil modulus of subgrade reaction, k, of 18 MPa/m. The slab-on-grade unit should float independently of all load-bearing walls and columns.

### 6.5    Excavation and Backfilling

The native sand and silty clay crust encountered at this site should be considered as Type 3 soils as defined by the Occupational Health and Safety Act and, therefore, excavation side slopes are required to be no steeper than 1 horizontal to 1 vertical from the bottom. Where excavations are required into the softer grey silty clay (Type 4 soil), the excavation slopes should be no steeper than 3 horizontal to 1 vertical from the bottom.

The groundwater level was encountered at a depth as shallow as 1 m one week after drilling. It has been our experience that the anticipated foundation soils are easily disturbed and are particularly sensitive to water softening. Excavation dewatering using conventional sumps and pumping techniques are expected to be applicable for this project based on the geotechnical information collected.

Foundation backfill should be placed and compacted in lifts. Care should be taken immediately adjacent to walls to avoid over-compaction of the soil resulting in damage to the walls.

Bedding for utilities should be placed in accordance with the pipe design requirements. It is recommended that a minimum of 150 to 200 mm OPSS Granular A be placed below the pipe invert as bedding material. Granular pipe back-fill placed above the invert should consist of OPSS Granular A or Granular B. A minimum of 300 mm vertical and side cover should be provided. These materials should be compacted to at least 95% of Standard Proctor maximum dry density.

Backfill for service trenches in landscaped areas may consist of excavated material replaced and compacted in lifts. Where the service trenches extend below paved areas, the trench should be backfilled with OPSS Granular B from the top of the pipe backfill material to within 1.2 m of the proposed pavement surface. This material should be placed in lifts and compacted to at least 95% of Standard Proctor maximum dry density. The material used within the upper 1.2 m and below the sub-grade line should be similar to that exposed in the trench walls to prevent differential frost heave. This material should be placed in lifts and compacted to at least 95% of Standard Proctor maximum dry density.

**EXAMPLE 15** *(continued)*

### 6.6    Earthquake Considerations

As outlined in the National Building Code of Canada (NBCC), 1990, buildings and their foundations must be designed to resist a minimum earthquake force. The NBCC formula for obtaining the minimum earthquake force is dependent upon several factors, four of which are the Foundation Factor, Zonal Velocity Ratio, and the Acceleration and Velocity Related Seismic Zones. The recommended Foundation Factor, F, is 2.0 for the soils encountered at this site. The Zonal Velocity Ratio, v, of 0.10, the Acceleration Related Seismic Zone, Za, of 4 and the Velocity Related Seismic Zone, Zv, of 2 are recommended for this site based on the NBCC.

### 6.7    Pavement Structure

The subgrade in paved areas should be prepared as described in Section 6.2 above. Assuming that the parking areas will be used mostly by passenger vehicles, and the access roads will be used by delivery trucks and fire vehicles, the following minimum pavement designs are recommended:

|  | Passenger Vehicle Parking Area | Access Roads |
|---|---|---|
| Asphaltic Concrete | 50 mm | 80 mm (2 lifts) |
| OPSS Granular A | 150 mm | 150 mm |
| OPSS Granular B | 300 mm | 450 mm |

All materials should be tested and approved by a geotechnical engineer prior to delivery to the site. Both the OPSS Granular A and Granular B materials should be compacted to at least 100% Standard Proctor maximum dry density.

### 7.0    CLOSURE

The recommendations presented in the report are in accordance with our present understanding of the project. A soils investigation is a random sampling of a site. Should any condition at the site be encountered which differs from those at the test locations, we require that we be notified immediately in order to permit reassessment of our recommendations.

We trust the above information meets with your requirements. Should you have any questions or require further information, please do not hesitate to contact us.

Thank you for the opportunity to be of service to you.

Yours very truly,

**Martin & Koffman**
Michael A. Corbett, M.Sc., P.Eng.
Gloria J. Kack, M.E.Sc., P.Eng.

7

**EXAMPLE 15** *(continued)*

**APPENDIX I**
**SYMBOLS AND TERMS USED ON BOREHOLE AND TEST PIT RECORDS**

**SOIL DESCRIPTION**

Terminology describing common soil genesis:

| | | |
|---|---|---|
| *Topsoil* | – | mixture of soil and humus capable of supporting good vegetation growth |
| *Peat* | – | fibrous aggregate of visible and invisible fragments of decayed organic matter |
| *Till* | – | unstratified glacial deposit which may range from clay to boulders |
| *Fill* | – | any materials below the surface identified as placed by humans (excluding buried services) |

Terminology describing soil structure:

| | | |
|---|---|---|
| *Desiccated* | – | having visible signs of weathering by oxidation of clay minerals, shrinkage cracks, etc. |
| *Fissured* | – | having cracks, and hence a blocky structure |
| *Varved* | – | composed of regular alternating layers of silt and clay |
| *Stratified* | – | composed of alternating successions of different soil types, e.g., silt and sand |
| *Layer* | – | > 75 mm |
| *Seam* | – | 2 mm to 75 mm |
| *Parting* | – | < 2 mm |
| *Well Graded* | – | having wide range in grain sizes and substantial amounts of all intermediate particle sizes |
| *Uniformly Graded* | – | predominantly of one grain size |

Terminology describing soils on the basis of grain size and plasticity is based on the Unified Soil Classification System (USCS) (ASTM D-2488). The classification excludes particles larger than 76 mm (3 inches). This system provides a group symbol (e.g., SM) and group name (e.g., silty sand) for identification.

Terminology describing materials outside the USCS (e.g., particles larger than 76 mm, visible organic matter, construction debris) is based upon the proportion of these materials present:

| | |
|---|---|
| *Trace, or occasional* | Less than 10% |
| *Some* | 10–20% |

The standard terminology to describe cohesionless soils includes the compactness (formerly "relative density"), as determined by laboratory test or by the Standard Penetration Test 'N' value.

8

**EXAMPLE 15** *(continued)*

| Relative Density | 'N' Value | Compactness % |
|---|---|---|
| Very Loose | <4 | <15 |
| Loose | 4–10 | 15–35 |
| Compact | 10–30 | 35–65 |
| Dense | 30–50 | 65–85 |
| Very Dense | >50 | >85 |

The standard terminology to describe cohesive soils includes the consistency, which is based on undrained shear strength as measured by in-situ vane tests, penetrometer tests, unconfined compression tests, or occasionally by standard penetration tests.

| Consistency | Undrained Shear Strength | | 'N' Value |
|---|---|---|---|
| | kips/sq.ft. | kPa | |
| Very Soft | <0.25 | <12.5 | <2 |
| Soft | 0.25–0.5 | 12.5–25 | 2–4 |
| Firm | 0.5–1.0 | 25–50 | 4–8 |
| Stiff | 1.0–2.0 | 50–100 | 8–15 |
| Very Stiff | 2.0–4.0 | 100–200 | 15–30 |
| Hard | >4.0 | >200 | >30 |

**ROCK DESCRIPTION**

**Rock Quality Designation (RQD)**

The classification is based on a modified core-recovery percentage in which all pieces of sound core over 100 mm long are counted as recovery. The smaller pieces are considered to be due to close shearing, jointing, faulting, or weathering in the rock mass and are not counted. RQD was originally intended to be done on NW core; however, it can be used on different core sizes if the bulk of the fractures caused by drilling stresses are easily distinguishable from in-situ fractures.

| RQD | Rock Quality |
|---|---|
| 90–100 | Excellent, intact, very sound |
| 75–90 | Good, massive, moderately jointed or sound |
| 50–75 | Fair, blocky and seamy, fractured |
| 25–50 | Poor, shattered and very seamy or blocky, severely fractured |
| 0–25 | Very poor, crushed, very severely fractured |

9

**EXAMPLE 15** *(continued)*

Terminology describing rock mass:

| Spacing (mm) | Bedding, Laminations, Bands | Discontinuities |
|---|---|---|
| 2000–6000 | *Very Thick* | *Very Wide* |
| 600–2000 | *Thick* | *Wide* |
| 200–600 | *Medium* | *Moderate* |
| 60–200 | *Thin* | *Close* |
| 20–60 | *Very Thin* | *Very Close* |
| <20 | *Laminated* | *Extremely Close* |
| <6 | *Thinly Laminated* | |

| Strength Classification | Uniaxial Compressive Strength (MPa) |
|---|---|
| *Very Low* | 1–25 |
| *Low* | 25–50 |
| *Medium* | 50–100 |
| *High* | 100–200 |
| *Very High* | >200 |

Terminology describing weathering:

| | | |
|---|---|---|
| *Slight* | – | Weathering limited to the surface of major discontinuities. Typically iron stained. |
| *Moderate* | – | Weathering extends throughout rock mass. Rock is not friable. |
| *High* | – | Weathering extends throughout rock mass. Rock is friable. |

**STRATA PLOT**

Strata plots symbolize the soil or bedrock description. They are combinations of the following basic symbols:

Boulders Cobbles Gravel | Sand | Silt | Clay | Organics | Asphalt | Concrete | Fill | Igneous Bedrock | Meta-morphic Bedrock | Sedimentary Bedrock

**WATER LEVEL MEASUREMENT**

Borehole or Standpipe                    Piezometer

10

**EXAMPLE 15 *(continued)***

**SAMPLE TYPE**

| | |
|---|---|
| SS | Split spoon sample (obtained by performing the Standard Penetration Test) |
| ST | Shelby tube or thin wall tube |
| PS | Piston sample |
| BS | Bulk sample |
| WS | Wash sample |
| HQ, NQ, BQ, etc. | Rock core samples obtained with the use of standard size diamond drilling bits |

**'N' VALUE**

Numbers in this column are the results of the Standard Penetration Test: the number of blows of a 140 pound (64 kg) hammer falling 30 inches (760 mm) required to drive a 2 inch (50.8 mm) O.D. split spoon sampler one foot (305 mm) into the soil. For split spoon samples where insufficient penetration was achieved and 'N' values cannot be presented, the number of blows are reported over sampler penetration in millimetres (e.g., 50/75).

**OTHER TESTS**

| | | | |
|---|---|---|---|
| S | Sieve analysis | H | Hydrometer analysis |
| $G_s$ | Specific gravity of soil particles | $\gamma$ | Unit weight |
| k | Permeability (cm/sec) | C | Consolidation |
| | Single packer permeability test; test interval from depth shown to bottom of borehole | CD | Consolidated drained triaxial |
| | | CU | Consolidated undrained triaxial with pore pressure measurements |
| | Double packer permeability test; test interval as indicated | UU | Unconsolidated undrained triaxial |
| | | DS | Direct shear |
| | Falling head permeability test using casing | $Q_u$ | Unconfined compression |
| | Falling head permeability test using well point or piezometer | $I_p$ | Point Load Index ($I_p$ on Borehole Record equals $I_p(50)$; the index corrected to a reference diameter of 50 mm) |

11

**EXAMPLE 15** *(continued)*

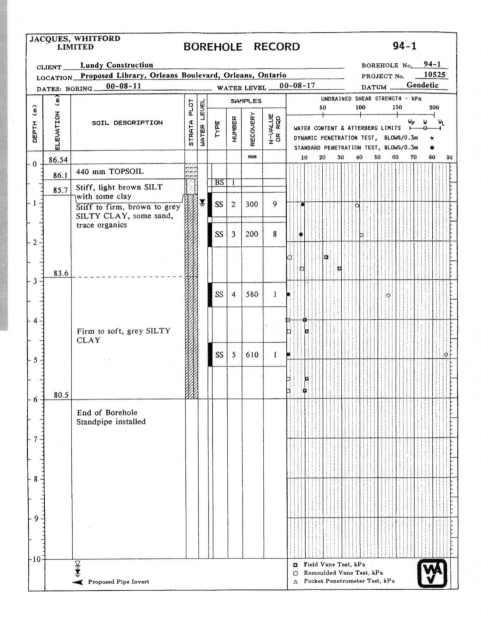

**EXAMPLE 15** *(continued)*

| JACQUES, WHITFORD LIMITED | BOREHOLE RECORD | 94-2 |
|---|---|---|

CLIENT __Lundy Construction__

LOCATION __Proposed Library, Orleans Boulevard, Orleans, Ontario__

DATES: BORING __00-08-11__     WATER LEVEL __00-08-17__

BOREHOLE No. __94-2__

PROJECT No. __10525__

DATUM __Geodetic__

| DEPTH (m) | ELEVATION (m) | SOIL DESCRIPTION | STRATA PLOT | WATER LEVEL | SAMPLES | | | | UNDRAINED SHEAR STRENGTH - kPa |
|---|---|---|---|---|---|---|---|---|---|
| | | | | | TYPE | NUMBER | RECOVERY mm | N-VALUE OR RQD | |

UNDRAINED SHEAR STRENGTH - kPa

50    100    150    200

WATER CONTENT & ATTERBERG LIMITS  $W_p$  W  $W_L$

DYNAMIC PENETRATION TEST, BLOWS/0.3m  ★

STANDARD PENETRATION TEST, BLOWS/0.3m  ●

10  20  30  40  50  60  70  80  90

| Depth | Elev | Description | Type | No. | Recovery | N-Value |
|---|---|---|---|---|---|---|
| 0 | 86.51 / 86.3 | 200 mm TOPSOIL | | | | |
| | 85.8 | Stiff, light brown SILT with some clay | | | | |
| 1 | | Stiff to firm, brown to grey SILTY CLAY, some sand, trace organics, occasional sand seam | SS | 1 | 270 | 10 |
| 2 | | | SS | 2 | 140 | 12 |
| 3 | 83.6 | | SS | 3 | 610 | 1 |
| 4 | | Firm to soft, grey SILTY CLAY | | | | |
| 5 | | | SS | 4 | 610 | 1 |
| 6 | 80.5 | End of Borehole Standpipe installed | | | | |

◀ Proposed Pipe Invert

□ Field Vane Test, kPa
□ Remoulded Vane Test, kPa
△ Pocket Penetrometer Test, kPa

**EXAMPLE 15** *(continued)*

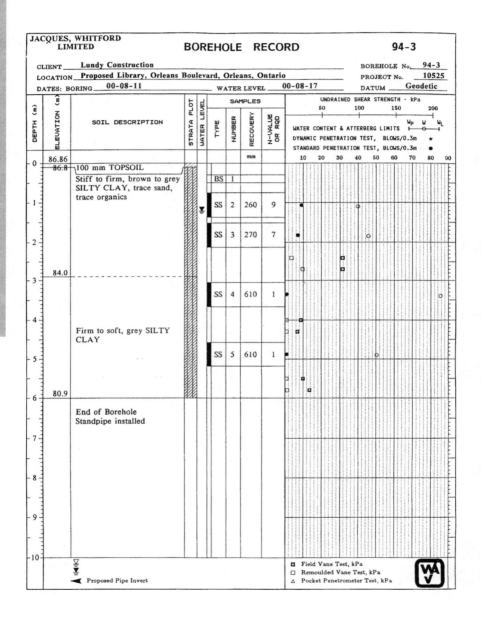

**EXAMPLE 15** *(continued)*

| JACQUES, WHITFORD LIMITED | BOREHOLE RECORD | 94-4 |
|---|---|---|

CLIENT **Lundy Construction**　　　　　BOREHOLE No. __94-4__

LOCATION **Proposed Library, Orleans Boulevard, Orleans, Ontario**　　　PROJECT No. __10525__

DATES: BORING ___00-08-11___　　　　WATER LEVEL _____　DATUM ___Geodetic___

| DEPTH (m) | ELEVATION (m) | SOIL DESCRIPTION | STRATA PLOT | WATER LEVEL | SAMPLES TYPE | NUMBER | RECOVERY | N-VALUE OR RQD | UNDRAINED SHEAR STRENGTH - kPa / WATER CONTENT & ATTERBERG LIMITS / DYNAMIC & STANDARD PENETRATION TEST |
|---|---|---|---|---|---|---|---|---|---|
| 0 | 86.62 |  |  |  |  |  |  | mm |  |
|  | 86.5 | 120 mm TOPSOIL |  |  |  |  |  |  |  |
|  | 86.2 | Dark brown silty clay, trace gravel, trace sand, trace asphalt: FILL |  |  | BS | 1 |  |  |  |
| 1 |  | Stiff to firm, brown to grey SILTY CLAY |  |  | SS | 2 | 170 | 10 |  |
|  |  |  |  |  | SS | 3 | 300 | 3 |  |
| 2 | 84.5 |  |  |  |  |  |  |  |  |
|  |  | End of Borehole |  |  |  |  |  |  |  |

UNDRAINED SHEAR STRENGTH - kPa  50  100  150  200

WATER CONTENT & ATTERBERG LIMITS $w_p$ w $w_L$

DYNAMIC PENETRATION TEST, BLOWS/0.3m ★

STANDARD PENETRATION TEST, BLOWS/0.3m ●

10 20 30 40 50 60 70 80 90

◀ Proposed Pipe Invert

□ Field Vane Test, kPa
□ Remoulded Vane Test, kPa
△ Pocket Penetrometer Test, kPa

**EXAMPLE 15** *(continued)*

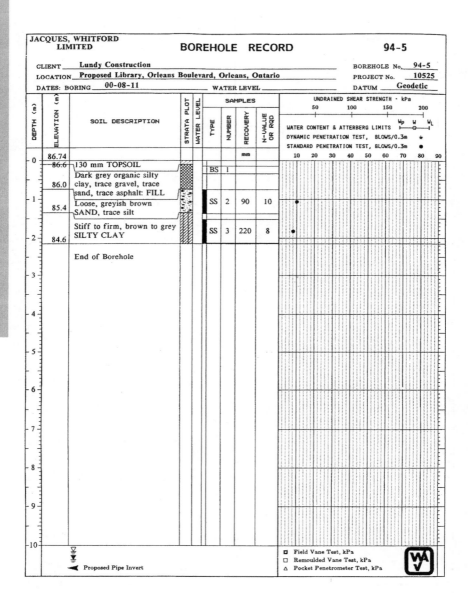

| JACQUES, WHITFORD LIMITED | | BOREHOLE RECORD | | 94-5 |
|---|---|---|---|---|

CLIENT __Lundy Construction__          BOREHOLE No. __94-5__
LOCATION __Proposed Library, Orleans Boulevard, Orleans, Ontario__          PROJECT No. __10525__
DATES: BORING __00-08-11__          WATER LEVEL          DATUM __Geodetic__

**EXAMPLE 15** *(continued)*

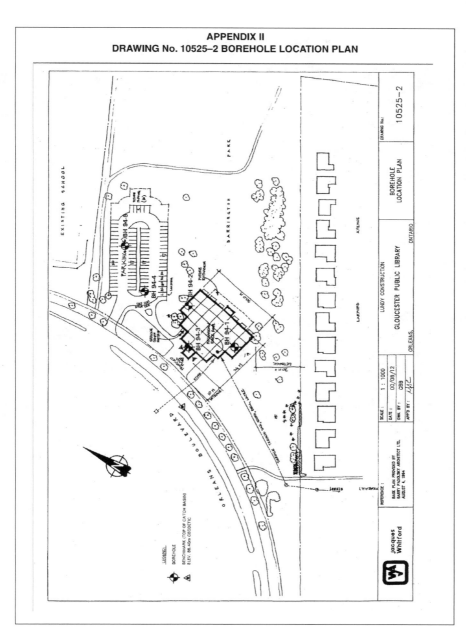

APPENDIX II
DRAWING No. 10525–2 BOREHOLE LOCATION PLAN

EXAMPLE 15 *(continued)*

DRAWING No. 10525–1  KEY PLAN

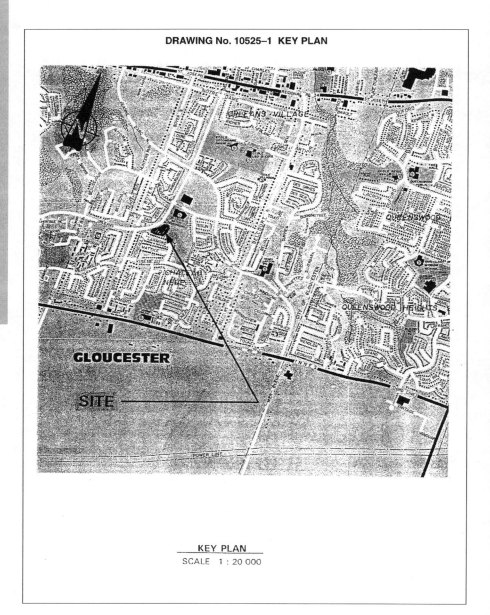

KEY PLAN
SCALE  1 : 20 000

EXAMPLE 15

# ABC Format 16: Job Letter and Résumé

## Abstract

- Apply for a specific job
- Refer to ad, mutual friend, or other source of information about the job
- (Optional) Briefly state how you can meet the main need of your potential employer

## Body

- Specify your understanding of the reader's main needs
- Provide main qualifications that satisfy these needs (but only highlight points from résumé—do *not* simply repeat all résumé information)
- Avoid mentioning weak points or deficiencies
- Keep body paragraphs to six or fewer lines
- Use a bulleted or numbered list if it helps draw attention to three or four main points
- Maintain the "you" attitude throughout

## Conclusion

- Tie the letter together with one main theme or selling point, as you would a sales letter
- Refer to your résumé
- Explain how and when the reader can contact you for an interview

### Helpful Hints

In the first examples of job letters and résumés that follow, note that one résumé is in what is called "chronological" format and the other is in "functional" format. Also included is a third résumé that combines the two formats. All three reflect a clear presentation of basic information about education, work experience, skills, and interests. However, they differ in what they emphasize, as explained below:

- James Sistrunk's résumé is considered "chronological." Because he has relevant full-time job experience, he gives it priority—with the most recent work listed first.
- Denise Sanborn's résumé is considered "functional." Because she has limited work experience, she wants to focus instead on the "functional" skills acquired in her part-time and summer jobs.
- Karen Patel's combined-format résumé lists two main skill sets as her main categories, under which particular full- and part-time jobs and their time periods are included.

Use the résumé format that best matches your background. Above all, keep your résumé looking clean. Remember that its purpose is only to get you to the next stage of the job process, the interview.

15 Park Road
Moncton, NB
E4P 9R9
August 6, 2003

Ms. Wendy Yancy
Director, Automotive Systems
XYZ Motor Company, Product Development Division
Moncton, NB E5S 1L8

Dear Ms. Yancy:

Recently I have been researching the leading national companies in automotive computer systems. Your job ad in the July 6 *National Business Employment Weekly* caught my eye because of XYZ's innovations in computer-controlled safety systems. I would like to apply for the automotive computer engineer job.

Your advertisement notes that experience in computer systems for machinery or robotic systems would be a plus. I have had extensive experience in the military with computer systems, ranging from a digital communications computer to an air traffic control training simulator. In addition, my college experience includes courses in computer engineering that have broadened my experience. I am eager to apply what I have learned to your company.

My mechanical knowledge was gained from growing up on my family's dairy farm. After watching and learning from my father, I learned to repair internal combustion engines, diesel engines, and hydraulic systems. Then for five years I managed the entire dairy operation.

With my training and hands-on experience, I believe I can contribute to your company. Please contact me at 506-882-2731 if you wish to arrange an interview.

Sincerely,

*James M. Sistrunk*

James M. Sistrunk

Enclosure: Résumé

**EXAMPLE 16  (pp. 132–137)**
Job Letter (block style) and chronological résumé
Source: *Technical Writing: A Practical Approach,* 3rd Canadian Edition (pp. 520–523) by W.S. Pfeiffer and J. Boogerd, 2004. Reprinted with permission by Pearson Education Canada Inc.

**James M. Sistrunk**
**15 Park Road**
**Moncton, NB E4P 9R9**
**(506) 882-2731**

**Professional Objective:**
　　To contribute to the research, design, and development of
　　automotive computer control systems

**Education:**
　　**B.Sc., Computer Engineering,** 2000–2004
　　**University of New Brunswick, Fredericton, NB**
　　Major concentration in Control Systems with minor in Industrial
　　Engineering. Courses included Microcomputer Systems, Digital
　　Control Systems, and several different programming courses.
　　**Computer Repair Technician Certification Training,** 1994–1998
　　**RCAF Training, CFB Trenton**
　　General Computer Systems Option with emphasis on mainframe
　　computers. Student leader in charge of processing and orientation
　　for new students from basic training.

**Career Development:**
　　**Computer Repair Technician,** RCAF, 1995–1999
　　NATO Clearance
　　Responsibilities and duties included:
　　　• Repair of computer systems
　　　• Documentation of work accomplished
　　　• Preventative maintenance inspections
　　　• Diagnostics and troubleshooting of equipment
　　Accomplishments include:
　　　• "Excellent" score during skills evaluation
　　　• Award of an Air Force Specialty Code "5" skill level
　　**Assistant Manager,** Spring Farm, Shediac, NB, 1990–1995
　　Responsible for dairy operations on this 500-acre farm. Developed
　　the management and technical skills; learned to repair
　　sophisticated farm equipment.

**Special Skills:**
　　Macintosh desktop publishing
　　IBM - MS DOS
　　Assembly Language
　　C++ Programming

**References:**
　　Available upon request

**EXAMPLE 16** *(continued)*

8 Cosmic Way, #245
Valleyfield, PQ J3E 2L7
September 3, 2003

Ms. Judith R. Gonzalez
Mercy Hospital
3023 Centre Avenue
Brampton, ON L3P 8R4

Dear Ms. Gonzalez:

My placement centre recently informed me about the Management Trainee opening with Mercy Hospital. As a business major with experience working in hospitals, I wish to apply for the position.

Your job advertisement notes that you seek candidates with a broad academic background in business and an interest in hospital management. At Conestoga College, I've taken extensive coursework in three major areas in business: finance, marketing, and personnel management. This broad-based academic curriculum has provided a solid foundation for a wide variety of management tasks at Mercy Hospital.

My summer and part-time employment also matches the needs of your position. While attending Conestoga, I've worked part-time and summers as an assistant in the Business Office at Grady Hospital. That experience has acquainted me with the basics of business management within the context of a mid-sized hospital, much like Mercy.

The enclosed résumé highlights the skills that match your Management Trainee opening. I would like the opportunity to talk with you in person and can be reached at 905-555-2642 for an interview.

Sincerely,

*Denise Ware Sanborn*

Denise Ware Sanborn

**EXAMPLE 16** *(continued)*

**Denise Ware Sanborn**
**8 Cosmic Way, #245**
**Valleyfield, PQ J3E 2L7**
**905-555-2642**

**Objective**
Entry-level management position in the health-care industry. Seek position
that includes exposure to a wide variety of management and business-
related tasks.

**Education**
Business Administration, June 2004
Conestoga College
Brampton, ON

Major:  Business Administration
Grade Point Average:  3.26 of possible 4.0, with 3.56 in all major courses
All college expenses financed by part-time and summer work at Grady
Hospital.

**Skills and Experience**
    Finance
        Helped with research for three fiscal-year budgets
        Developed new spreadsheet for monthly budget reports
        Wrote accounts payable correspondence
        Called on collections from insurance companies
    Marketing
        Solicited copy from managers for new brochure
        Designed and edited new brochure
        Participated in team visits to ten area physicians
        Wrote copy for one-page flyer
    Personnel
        Designed new performance appraisal form for secretarial staff
        Interviewed applicants for Maintenance Department jobs
        Coordinated annual training program for nursing staff

**Awards**
1999 Arden Award for best senior project in the Business Administration
Department (paper that examined latest developments in Total Quality
Management)

Dean's list for six semesters.

**References**
Academic and work references available upon request.

**EXAMPLE 16** *(continued)*

### Karen S. Patel

**Home:** (416) 555-2112                                    **Messages:** (416) 555-0111

| | |
|---|---|
| **OBJECTIVE** | Position as in-house technical writer and as trainer in communication skills |
| **EDUCATION** | **Technical Writer Program, December 2002**<br>Ryerson Polytechnic University |
| | **M.A. in English, June 2001**<br>Concordia University |
| | **B.A. in English, First Class Honours, June 1996**<br>University of Bombay, India |
| **EMPLOYMENT**<br><br>*Editing/*<br>*Writing* | **Public Relations, Toronto Board of Education, 2002 to present**<br>*Administrative Assistant:* Write press releases and conduct interviews. Publish news stories in local newspapers. Edit newsletter. |
| | **Hawk Newspapers, Montreal, 2000–2001**<br>*Concordia Internship:* Covered and reported special events; conducted interviews; assisted with proofreading, layout, headline count. Scanned newspapers for current events; conducted research for stories. Published feature stories. |
| *Teaching/*<br>*Research* | **Ryerson Polytechnic University, 2001–2002**<br>*Teaching Assistant:* Tutored English at the Writing Centre, answered "Grammar Hotline" phone questions, edited and critiqued student papers, taught English to non-English speakers and helped students prepare for exams. |
| | **Concordia University, 1999–2001**<br>*Teaching Assistant:* Taught business writing, supervised peer editing and in-class discussions, held student conferences, and graded student papers. |
| | *Research Assistant:* Verified material by checking facts, wrote brief reports related to research, researched information and bibliographies. |
| **COMPUTER SKILLS** | WordPerfect, Microsoft Word, Pagemaker, Unix, Excel |
| **REFERENCES** | Available upon request |

**EXAMPLE 16**

# Appendix B: Writing Handbook

*C*hapter 1 divided the writing process into three stages: planning, drafting, and revising. This appendix will help you fix problems that occur during the revision stage of writing. It includes alphabetized entries on style, grammar, and usage. These three terms are defined as follows:

**Style:** features such as word choice, sentence length, paragraph organization, and active and passive voice. These are matters of choice, not right and wrong. For example, both the wordy and concise versions of a passage may be grammatically correct, but the concise version is a better stylistic choice.

**Grammar:** actual rules that determine how language should be used, as opposed to stylistic options one can choose. Examples of such "right/wrong" issues include comma placement and correct use of modifiers.

**Usage:** contexts for the correct use of problem words—especially word pairs such as "effect/affect" and "complement/compliment."

Each entry in this appendix has two parts: an explanation of the meaning and one or more correct examples.

Of course, when you're preparing a document for your boss or client, you don't separate problems by style, grammar, or usage. You just want to produce a draft that is easy to read and free of errors. Thus all entries in this appendix are alphabetized for easy reference. Following are two separate tables of contents—alphabetical and topical:

## ALPHABETIZED TABLE OF CONTENTS

## TOPICAL TABLE OF CONTENTS

### Style

## A/An

These two words are different forms of the same article. "A" occurs before words that start with consonants or consonant sounds. Examples:

- a three-pronged plug
- a once-in-a-lifetime job ("once" begins with the consonant sound of *w*)
- a historic moment (many speakers and some writers mistakenly use "an" before "historic")

"An" occurs before words that begin with vowels or vowel sounds. Examples:

- an eager new employee
- an hour before closing

## A lot/Alot

The correct form is "a lot." Though acceptable in informal discourse, "a lot" usually should be replaced by more formal diction in technical writing. Example: "They retrieved many [*not* a lot of] soil samples from the construction site."

## Abbreviations

Technical writing uses many abbreviations. Without this shorthand form, you would end up writing much longer reports and proposals, without any additional content. Follow these seven basic rules in your use of abbreviations, paying special attention to the first three:

### ■ Rule 1: Do Not Use Abbreviations When Confusion May Result

When you want to use a term just once or twice and you are not certain your readers will understand an abbreviation, write out the term rather than abbreviating it. Example: "They were required to remove formaldehyde from the site, according to the directive from the Workers' Compensation Board." Even though "WCB" is the accepted abbreviation for this provincial agency, you should write out the name in full *if* you are using the term only once to an audience that may not understand it.

### ■ *Rule 2: Use Parentheses for Clarity*

When you use a term *more* than twice and are not certain that your readers will understand it, write out the term the first time it is used and place the abbreviation in parentheses. Then use the abbreviation in the rest of the document. In long reports or proposals, however, you may need to repeat the full term in key places. Example: "According to the directive from the Workers' Compensation Board (WCB), they were required to remove the formaldehyde from the construction site. Furthermore, the directive indicated that the builders could expect to be visited by WCB inspectors every other week."

### ■ *Rule 3: Include a Glossary When There Are Many Abbreviations*

When your document contains many abbreviations that may not be understood by all readers, include a well-marked glossary at the beginning or end of the document. A glossary simply collects all the terms and abbreviations and places them in one location, for easy reference.

### ■ *Rule 4: Use Abbreviations for Units of Measure*

Most technical documents use abbreviations for units of measure. Do not include a period unless the abbreviation could be confused with a word. Examples: km, cm, ml, in., gal., and g. Note that units-of-measurement abbreviations have the same form for both singular and plural amounts. Examples: 0.5 cm, 1 cm, 5 cm.

### ■ *Rule 5: Avoid Spacing and Periods*

Avoid internal spacing and internal periods in most abbreviations that contain all capital letters. Examples: ASTM, EPA, ASEE. Exceptions include professional titles and degrees such as P.E., B.Sc., and B.A., and geographical terms such as U.S.A. and U.K.

### ■ *Rule 6: Be Careful with Company Names*

Abbreviate a company or other organizational name only when you are sure that officials from the organization consider the abbreviation appropriate. IBM (for the company) and CBC (for the public corporation) are two commonly accepted organizational abbreviations. When in doubt, follow Rule 2—write the name in full the first time it is used, followed by the abbreviation in parentheses.

## ■ *Rule 7: Use These Common Abbreviations*

These common abbreviations are appropriate for most writing in your technical or business career. They are placed here in three main categories: measurements, locations, and titles.

**Measurements:** Use these abbreviations only when you place numbers before the measurement.

| | |
|---|---|
| ac | alternating current |
| amp | ampere |
| bbl | barrel |
| Btu | British thermal unit |
| bu | bushel |
| C | Celsius |
| cal | calorie |
| cc | cubic centimetre |
| circ | circumference |
| cm | centimetre |
| $cm^2$ | square centimetre |
| $cm^3$ | cubic centimetre |
| cos | cosine |
| cot | cotangent |
| cps | cycles per second |
| cu ft | cubic feet |
| dB | decibel |
| dc | direct current |
| dm | decimeter |
| doz *or* dz | dozen |
| F | Fahrenheit |
| f | farad |
| fbm | foot board measure |
| fig. | figure |
| fl oz | fluid ounce |

| | |
|---|---|
| FM | frequency modulation |
| fp | foot pound |
| ft | foot (feet) |
| g | gram |
| gal. | gallon |
| gpm | gallons per minute |
| hp | horsepower |
| hr | hour |
| Hz | hertz |
| in. | inch |
| j | joule |
| K | Kelvin |
| ke | kinetic energy |
| kg | kilogram |
| km | kilometre |
| $km^2$ | square kilometre |
| kw | kilowatt |
| kwh | kilowatt-hour |
| l | litre |
| lb | pound |
| lin | linear |
| lm | lumen |
| log. | logarithm |
| m | metre |
| mm | millimetre |
| min | minute |
| oz | ounce |
| ppm | parts per million |
| psf | pounds per square foot |
| psi | pounds per square inch |
| pt | pint |
| qt | quart |
| rev | revolution |
| rpm | revolutions per minute |
| sec | second |
| sq | square |
| sq ft | square foot (feet) |
| t | tonne |

| tan. | tangent |
| v | volt |
| va | volt-ampere |
| w | watt |
| wk | week |
| wl | wavelength |
| yd | yard |
| yr | year |

**Locations:** Use these common abbreviations for addresses (on envelopes and letters, for example), but write out the words in full in other contexts.

| AB | Alberta | NU | Nunavut |
| BC | British Columbia | ON | Ontario |
| MB | Manitoba | PE | Prince Edward Island |
| NB | New Brunswick | PQ | Quebec |
| NF | Newfoundland | SK | Saskatchewan |
| NT | Northwest Territories | YT | Yukon |
| NS | Nova Scotia | | |

| AL | Alabama | NM | New Mexico |
| AK | Alaska | NY | New York |
| AS | American Samoa | NC | North Carolina |
| AZ | Arizona | ND | North Dakota |
| AR | Arkansas | OH | Ohio |
| CA | California | OK | Oklahoma |
| GA | Georgia | CZ | Canal Zone |
| GU | Guam | CO | Colorado |
| HI | Hawaii | CT | Connecticut |
| ID | Idaho | DE | Delaware |
| IL | Illinois | DC | District of Columbia |
| IN | Indiana | FL | Florida |
| IA | Iowa | OR | Oregon |
| KS | Kansas | PA | Pennsylvania |
| KY | Kentucky | PR | Puerto Rico |
| LA | Louisiana | RI | Rhode Island |
| ME | Maine | SC | South Carolina |

| | | | |
|---|---|---|---|
| MD | Maryland | SD | South Dakota |
| MA | Massachusetts | TN | Tennessee |
| MI | Michigan | TX | Texas |
| MN | Minnesota | UT | Utah |
| MS | Mississippi | VT | Vermont |
| MO | Missouri | VI | Virgin Islands |
| MT | Montana | VA | Virginia |
| NE | Nebraska | WA | Washington |
| NV | Nevada | WV | West Virginia |
| NH | New Hampshire | WI | Wisconsin |
| NJ | New Jersey | WY | Wyoming |

**Titles:** Some of these abbreviations go before the name (such as Dr., Ms., and Messrs.), while others go after the name (such as university degrees, Jr., and Sr.).

| | |
|---|---|
| B.A. | Bachelor of Arts |
| B.Sc. | Bachelor of Science |
| Dr. | Doctor (used mainly with medical and dental degrees but also with other doctorates) |
| Drs. | plural of Dr. |
| D.V.M. | Doctor of Veterinary Medicine |
| Hon. | Honourable |
| Jr. | Junior |
| LL.D. | Doctor of Laws |
| M.A. | Master of Arts |
| M.Sc. | Master of Science |
| M.D. | Doctor of Medicine |
| Messrs. | Plural of Mr. |
| Mr. | Mister |
| Mrs. | used to designate married, widowed, or divorced women. (Note that many women prefer not to be known by their marital status.) |
| Ms. | used increasingly for all women, especially when the writer is uncertain about a woman's marital status |
| Ph.D. | Doctor of Philosophy |
| Sr. | Senior |

## ACCEPT/EXCEPT

These words have different meanings and often are different parts of speech. *Accept* is a verb that means "to receive." *Except* is a preposition or verb and means "to make an exception or special case of." Examples:

- I *accepted* the service award from my office manager.
- Everyone *except* Jonah attended the marine science lecture.
- The company president *excepted* me from the meeting because I had an important sales call to make the same day.

## ACCURATE WORDING

Good technical writing style demands accuracy in phrasing. Indeed, many technical professionals place their reputation and even their financial lives on the line with every document that goes out their door. That fact makes clear the importance of taking your time on any editing pass that deals with accuracy of phrasing. Accuracy often demands more words, not fewer. The main rule, then, is never to sacrifice clarity for conciseness. Following are some rules for writing accurately. They also will help you to avoid unnecessary exposure to liability.

### Distinguish Facts from Opinions

Always identify your opinions and judgments as such by using phrases like "we recommend," "we believe," "we suggest," and "in our opinion." If you want to avoid repetitious use of these phrases, group your opinions into a series or list. Thus a single lead-in can indicate to the reader that opinions, not facts, are forthcoming. Examples:

- In our opinion, spread footings would be an acceptable foundation for the building you plan at the site.
- On the basis of our site visit and our experience at similar sites, we believe that (1) _____, (2) _____, and (3) _____.

### Include Obvious Qualifying Statements When Needed

Be aware of possible misinterpretations by those who may not know that even technical fields can be inexact. Write carefully, but without becoming overly defensive. In other words, your readers—especially those who are nontechnical—want to know what you did do *and* what you did not do. Example:

> Our summary of soil conditions is based only on information obtained during a brief visit to the site. We did not drill any soil borings.

## Avoid Absolutes Unless You Mean Them

Some words may convey a stronger meaning than you intend. One notable example is *minimize,* which means to reduce to the lowest possible level or amount. If a report claims that a particular piece of equipment will "minimize" breakdowns on the assembly line, the passage could be interpreted as an absolute commitment. In theory, the reader could consider any breakdown at all to be a violation of the report's implications. If instead the writer had used the verb *limit* or *reduce,* the wording would have been more accurate and less open to misunderstanding.

> **Original:** If you follow our recommendations, pollution will be minimized at the site.

> **Revision:** If you follow our recommendations, pollution will be greatly reduced at the site.

The original version would be correct only if the writers were able to guarantee that their recommendations would lead to the lowest possible level of pollution.

## ACTIVE AND PASSIVE VOICE

This entry defines the active and passive voices and gives examples of each. It also lists some guidelines for using both voices.

## The Meaning of Active and Passive

Active-voice sentences emphasize the person (or thing) performing the action—that is, somebody (or something) does something ("Omar completed the field study yesterday"). Passive-voice sentences emphasize the action itself—that is, something is being done by somebody ("The field study was completed [by Omar] yesterday"). Here are some other examples of the same thoughts expressed in first the active and then the passive voice:

### Examples: Active Voice

1. We *reviewed* aerial photographs in our initial assessment of possible fault activity at the site.
2. The study *revealed* that three underground storage tanks had leaked unleaded gasoline into the soil.
3. We *recommend* that you use a minimum concrete thickness of 15 cm for residential subdivision streets.

### Examples: Passive Voice

1. Aerial photographs *were reviewed* [by us] in our initial assessment of possible fault activity at the site.
2. The fact that three underground storage tanks had been leaking unleaded gasoline into the soil *was revealed* in the study.
3. *It is recommended* that you use a minimum concrete thickness of 15 cm for residential concrete streets.

Note that passive constructions are wordier than active ones. They tend to leave out the person or thing doing the action. Although occasionally this impersonal approach is appropriate, often the reader becomes frustrated by writing that does not indicate who or what is doing something.

## Using Active and Passive Voice

The fact is that both the active and passive voice have a role in writing. Knowing when to use each is the key. Here are a few guidelines that will help:

### Use the Active Voice When You Want to Do the Following:

1. Emphasize who is responsible for an action (*"We recommend* that you consider our firm for the work").
2. Stress the name of a company, whether yours or the reader's (*"PineBluff Contracting has expressed* interest in receiving bids for the Baytown project").
3. Rewrite a top-heavy sentence so that the main idea is up front (*"Figure 1 shows* the approximate locations of the cars that derailed from the northbound freight train").
4. Pare down the verbiage in your writing, because the active voice is always a shorter construction (see the active and passive examples in previous subsections).

### Use the Passive Voice When You Want to Do the Following:

1. Emphasize the action rather than the person performing it (*"Samples will be sent* directly from the site to our laboratory in Sacramento").

2. Avoid the kind of egocentric tone that results from repetitious use of "I," "we," and the name of your company (*The project will be directed* by two programmers from our Regina office").
3. Break the monotony of writing that relies too heavily on active-voice sentences.

Technical and business writing depends far too much on the passive voice. This stylistic error results in part from the common misperception that passive writing is more "objective." In fact, overuse of passives only makes writing more tedious to read. In modern business and technical writing, most readers prefer the active voice.

## *ADVICE/ADVISE/INFORM*

*Advice* is a noun that means "suggestion or recommendation." *Advise* is a verb that means "to suggest or recommend." Do not use the verb *advise* as a substitute for *inform,* which means simply "to provide information." Examples:

- The consultant gave us *advice* on starting a new retirement plan for our employees.
- She *advised* us that a pension plan would be useful for all our employees.
- She *informed* [not *advised*] her clients that they would receive her final report by March 15.

## *AFFECT/EFFECT*

These two words cause much confusion. The key to using them correctly is remembering two simple sentences that cover most (but, unfortunately, not all) usage:

1. *Affect* with an "a" is a verb meaning "to influence."
2. *Effect* with an "e" is a noun meaning "result."

Here is one main exception you also need to know: In special instances, *effect* can be a verb that means "to bring about," as in "He effected considerable change when he became a manager." Examples:

- His progressive leadership greatly *affected* the company's future.
- One *effect* of securing the large government contract was the hiring of several more accountants.
- The president's belief in the future of microcomputers *effected* change in the company's approach to office management. (Less wordy alternative: substitute *changed* for *effected change in.*)

## AGREE TO/AGREE WITH

*Agree to* means that you have *consented to* an arrangement, offer, proposal, etc. *Agree with* suggests only that you are *in harmony with* a certain statement, idea, person, etc. Examples:

- Representatives from our firm *agreed to* alter the contract to reflect the new scope of work.
- We *agree with* you that more study may be needed before the plant is built.

## ALL RIGHT/ALRIGHT

*All right* is an acceptable spelling; *alright* is not. *All right* is an adjective that means "acceptable," an exclamation that means "outstanding," or a phrase that means "correct." Examples:

- Sharon suggested that the advertising copy was *all right* for now but that she would want changes next month.
- Upon seeing his article in print, Zach exclaimed *"All right!"*
- The five classmates were *all right* in their response to the trick questions on the quiz.

## ALL TOGETHER/ALTOGETHER

*All together* is used when items or people are being considered in a group, are working in concert, or are in the same location. *Altogether* is a synonym for "entirely" or "completely." Examples:

- *All together,* the sales team included 50 employees from 15 offices.
- The three firms were *all together* in their support of the agency's plan.
- The managers were *all together* in Charlottetown for the conference.
- There were *altogether* too many pedestrians walking near the dangerous intersection.

## ALLUSION/ILLUSION/DELUSION/ELUSION

These similar-sounding words have distinct meanings. Here is a summary of the differences:

1. **Allusion:** a noun meaning "reference," as in your making an allusion to your vacation in a speech. The related verb is *allude.*
2. **Illusion:** a noun meaning "misunderstanding or false perception." It can be physical (as in seeing a mirage) or mental (as in having the false impression that your hair is not thinning when it is).
3. **Delusion:** a noun meaning a belief based on self-deception. Unlike *illusion,* the word conveys a much stronger sense that someone is out of touch with reality, as in having "delusions of grandeur." The related verb is *delude.*
4. **Elusion:** a noun meaning "the act of escaping or avoiding." The more common form is the verb *elude,* meaning "to escape or avoid."

Examples:

- His report included an *allusion* to the upcoming visit by the government agency in charge of accreditation.
- She harboured an *illusion* that she was certain to receive the promotion. In fact, her supervisor preferred another department member with more experience.
- He had *delusions* that he soon would become company president, even though he started just last week in the mailroom.
- The main point of the report *eluded* him because there was no executive summary.

## ALREADY/ALL READY

*All ready* is a phrase that means "everyone is prepared," whereas *already* is an adverb that means something is finished or completed. Examples:

- They were *all ready* for the presentation to the client.
- George had *already* arrived at the office before the rest of his proposal team members had even left their homes.

## ALTERNATELY/ALTERNATIVELY

Because many readers are aware of the distinction between these two words, any misuse can cause embarrassment or even misunderstanding. Follow these guidelines for correct use.

## *Alternately*

As a derivative of *alternate, alternately* is best reserved for events or actions that occur "in turns." Example:

> They used a backhoe during some portions of the project. *Alternately,* they switched to using hand shovels.

## *Alternatively*

A derivative of *alternative, alternatively* should be used when two or more choices are being considered. Example:

> We suggest that you use deep foundations at the site. *Alternatively,* you could consider spread footings.

## *ALUMNA/ALUMNAE/ALUMNUS/ALUMNI*

These terms are derived directly from Latin. An *alumna* is a female graduate, whereas an *alumnus* is a male graduate. The plural forms are *alumnae* for females and *alumni* for males. Some writers prefer to use the plural form *alumni* in situations that involve both male and female graduates. However, the different masculine and feminine forms still are maintained in formal English. Examples:

- As a recent *alumna,* she often helped solicit donations from other *alumnae* of her university.
- He was considered a loyal *alumnus* of the university. Along with 100 other *alumni,* he volunteered every month at the Big Brothers Association of downtown Montréal.

## *AMOUNT/NUMBER*

*Amount* is used in reference to items that *cannot* be counted, whereas *number* is used to indicate items that *can* be counted. Examples:

- In the last year we have greatly increased the *amount* of computer paper ordered for the Vancouver office.
- The last year has seen a huge increase in the *number* [not *amount*] of boxes of computer paper ordered for the Vancouver office.

## *AND/OR*

This awkward expression probably has its origins in legal writing. It means that there are three separate options to be considered: the item before *and/or,* the item after *and/or,* or both items.

Avoid *and/or* because readers may find it confusing, visually awkward, or both. Instead, replace it with the structure used in the previous sentence. That is, write "A, B, or both," *not* "A and/or B." Example:

> The management trainee was permitted to select two seminars from the areas of computer hardware, communication skills, or both [not *computer hardware and/or communication skills*].

## *ANTICIPATE/EXPECT*

These two words are *not* synonyms. Their meanings are distinctly different. *Anticipate* is used when you mean to suggest or state that steps have been taken *beforehand* to prepare for a situation. *Expect* means only that you consider something likely to occur. Examples:

- *Anticipating* that the contract will be successfully negotiated, Jones Engineering is hiring three new hydrologists.
- We *expect* [not *anticipate*] that you will encounter semi-cohesive and cohesive soils in your excavations at the Pine Avenue site.

## *APOSTROPHES*

Apostrophes can be used for contractions, for some plurals, and for possessives. Only the latter two uses cause confusion. Use an apostrophe to indicate the plural form of a word as a word. Example:

> That redundant paragraph contained seven *area*'s and three *factor*'s in only five sentences.

Although some writers also use apostrophes to form the plurals of numbers and full-cap abbreviations, the current tendency is to include only the "s." Examples:

> 7s, ABCs, PCBs, P.E.s.

As for possessives, grammar rules seem to vary, depending on the reference book you're reading. Here are some simple guidelines that reflect this book's view of the best current usage:

### Multi-Syllabic Nouns Ending in "s"

Form the possessive of multi-syllabic nouns that end in "s" by adding just an apostrophe, whether the nouns are singular or plural. Examples:

> actress' costume, genius' test score, the three technicians' samples, Jesus' parables, the companies' joint project

### Single-Syllable Nouns Ending in "s"

Form the possessive of single-syllable nouns ending in "s" or an "s" sound by adding an apostrophe plus "s." Examples:

> Hoss's horse, Rex's song, the boss's progress report

### All Nouns Not Ending in "s"

Form the possessive of all singular and plural nouns not ending in "s" by adding an apostrophe plus "s." Examples:

> the man's hat, the men's team, the company's policy

### Paired Nouns

Form the possessive of paired nouns by first determining whether there is joint ownership or individual ownership. For joint ownership, make only the last noun possessive. For individual ownership, make both nouns possessive. Examples:

> Susan and Terry's project was entered in the science fair, but Tom's and Scott's projects were not.

### APT/LIABLE/LIKELY

Maintain the distinctions in these three similar words.

1. *Apt* is an adjective that means "appropriate," "suitable," or "has an aptitude for."
2. *Liable* is an adjective that means "legally obligated" or "subject to."
3. *Likely* is either an adjective that means "probable" or "promising" or an adverb that means "probably." As an adverb, it should be preceded by a qualifier such as *quite*.

Examples:

- The successful advertising campaign showed that she could select an *apt* phrase for selling products.
- Jonathan is *apt* at running good meetings. He always hands out an agenda and always ends on time.
- The contract makes clear who is *liable* for any on-site damage.
- Completing the warehouse without an inspection will make the contractor *liable* to lawsuits from the owner.
- A *likely* result of the investigation will be a change in the law. [*likely* as an adjective]
- The investigation will quite *likely* result in a change in the law. [*likely* as an adverb]

## ASSURE/ENSURE/INSURE

As a verb meaning "to promise," *assure* is used in reference to people, as in "We want to assure you that our crews will strive to complete the project on time." *Assure* and its derivatives (like *assurance*) should be used with care in technical contexts, for these words can be viewed as a promise or guarantee.

The synonyms *ensure* and *insure* are verbs meaning to "make certain." Like *assure,* they imply a level of certainty that is not always appropriate in engineering and the sciences. When their use is deemed appropriate, the preferred word is *ensure;* reserve *insure* for sentences in which the context is insurance. Examples:

- I can *assure* you that our representatives will be on site to answer questions that the subcontractor may have.
- To *ensure* that the project stays within schedule, we are building in 10 extra days for bad weather. (An alternative that expresses less certainty and obligation: *So that* the project stays within schedule, we are building in 10 extra days for bad weather.)
- We *insured* the truck for $15,000.

## AUGMENT/SUPPLEMENT

*Augment* is a verb that means "to increase in size, weight, number, or importance." *Supplement* is either (1) a verb that means to "add to" something to make it complete or to make up for a deficiency *or* (2) a noun that means "the thing that has been added." Examples:

- The power company supervisor decided to *augment* the line crews in five counties.
- He *supplemented* the deficient audit report by adding the three annual statements requested by the auditors.
- The three accounting *supplements* helped support the conclusions of the audit report.

## AWHILE/A WHILE

Although similar in meaning, this pair is used differently. *Awhile* is an adverb that means "for a short time." Because *for* is already a part of its definition, the word cannot be preceded by the proposition *for*. The noun *while*, however, can be preceded by the two words *for a*, giving it essentially the same meaning as *awhile*. Examples:

- Kirk waited *awhile* before trying to restart the generator.
- Kirk waited *for a while* before trying to restart the generator.

## BALANCE/REMAINDER/REST

*Balance* should be used as a synonym for *remainder* only in the context of financial affairs. *Remainder* and *rest* are synonyms to be used in other non-financial contexts. Examples:

- The account had a *balance* of $500, which was enough to avoid a service charge.
- The *remainder* [or *rest*, but not *balance*] of the day will be spent on training in oral presentations for proposals.
- During the *rest* [not *balance*] of the session, we learned about the new office equipment.

## BECAUSE/SINCE

Maintain the distinction between these two words. *Because* establishes a cause-effect relationship, whereas *since* is associated with time. Examples:

- *Because* he left at 3 p.m., he was able to avoid rush hour.
- *Since* last week, her manufacturing team completed 3,000 units.

Note that *because* should not be used in the wordy construction "the reason is because." Examples:

- John wants the transfer *because* he needs the experience working at another office. [*not* "The reason John needs the transfer is because he needs the experience working at another office."]
- The ship sank *because* it was overloaded. [*not* "The reason the ship sank was because it was overloaded."]

## BETWEEN/AMONG

The distinction between these two words has become somewhat blurred. However, many readers still prefer to see *between* used with reference to only two items and *among* used for three or more items. Examples:

- The agreement was just *between* my supervisor and me. No one else in the group knew about it.
- The proposal was circulated *among* all five members of the writing team.
- *Among* Sally, Todd, and Fran, there was little agreement about the long-term benefits of the project.

## BI-/SEMI-/BIANNUAL/BIENNIAL

The prefixes *bi* and *semi* can cause confusion. Generally, *bi* means "every two years, months, weeks, etc.," whereas *semi* means "twice a year, month, week, etc." Yet many readers get confused by the difference, especially when they are confronted with a notable exception such as *biannual* (which means twice a year) and *biennial* (which means every two years).

Your goal, as always, is clarity for the reader. Therefore, it is best to write out meanings in clear prose, rather than relying on prefixes that may not be understood. Examples:

- We get paid twice a month [preferable to *semimonthly* or *biweekly*].
- The part-time editor submits articles every other month [preferable to *bimonthly*].
- We hold a company social gathering twice a year [preferable to *biannually* or *semiannually*].
- The auditor inspects our safety files every two years [preferable to *biennially*].

## BRACKETS

Use a pair of brackets (1) to set off explanatory material already contained within another parenthetical statement (see Parentheses entry in this appendix) or (2) to draw attention to a comment that you, as the writer, are making within a passage you are quoting. Examples:

> Two of our studies have shown that Colony Dam satisfies safety standards. (See Figure 4-3 [Dam Safety Record] for a complete record of our findings.) In addition, the county engineer, Greg Parker, has a letter on file that will give further assurance to homeowners on the lake. Parker notes the following in his letter: "After finishing my three-month study [Parker completed it in July 1995], I have concluded that the Colony Dam meets all required safety standards."

## CAPITAL/CAPITOL

*Capital* is a noun whose main meanings are (1) a city or town that is a government centre, (2) wealth or resources, or (3) net worth of a business or the investment that has been made in the business by owners. *Capital* can also be an adjective meaning (1) "excellent," (2) "primary," or (3) "related to the death penalty." Finally, *capital* can be a noun or adjective referring to upper-case letters.

- The *capital* of Nova Scotia is Halifax.
- Our family *capital* was reduced by the tornado and hurricane.
- She had invested significant *capital* in the carpet factory.
- Their proposal contained some *capital* ideas that would open new opportunities for our firm.
- In some countries, armed robbery is a *capital* offence.

## CAPITALIZATION

As a rule, you should capitalize names of specific people, places, and things—sometimes called "proper" nouns. For example, capitalize specific streets, towns, trademarks, geological eras, planets, groups of stars, days of the week, months of the year, names of organizations, holidays, and colleges. Nonspecific nouns—called "common" nouns—are not capitalized.

Of course, if it were this easy there wouldn't be so much confusion about capitalization. There is a tendency in business to overuse capitalization, as in the use of capitals with titles of positions. An example of improper usage follows: "The Director of Marketing visited our office last week." Excessive use of capitals appears pompous and is inappropriate in technical writing. The best practice today includes limited, judicious use of capitals. When in doubt, leave it lowercase. Here are the most frequently capitalized items:

## *Major Words in Titles of Books and Articles*

Capitalize prepositions and articles only when they are the first words in titles. Examples:

- *For Whom the Bell Tolls*
- *In Search of Excellence*
- *The Power of Positive Thinking*

## *Names of Specific Places and Geographical Locations*

Examples:

- Peace Tower
- Olympic Stadium
- Newcastle, New Brunswick
- Prince Edward County

## *Names of Aircraft and Ships*

Examples:

- The Flying Dutchman
- HMS *Athabasca*
- *Nousuch*

## *Names of Departments, Offices, and Committees in an Organization*

Examples:

- Personnel Department
- International Division
- Benefits Committee

However, when shorthand terms are used for these entities, capitals are not used. Example: "Being an elected member of the Benefits Committee, I am concerned that the committee has not met in six months."

## *Titles That Come before Names*

Accepted practice calls for capitalizing titles only when they come directly before the name of the person who holds the title. When titles are used by themselves or follow a person's name, usually they are not capitalized. Examples:

- After breakfast, Chancellor Hairston opened the session.
- To our chagrin, Councilwoman Sharon Jones has served for nine years.

- We thought Professor Ginsberg gave a fine lecture.
- Sunita Mehta, a professor in the Math Department, is on leave.
- Rob Herrera, president of BGK, Inc., took a well-deserved vacation.
- Our company president was visiting the Singapore office.

The most noteworthy exceptions to this rule are heads of state; such titles are usually capitalized in any context. There are few other exceptions. If a company insists on breaking this rule—as in policy documents—it should capitalize *all* positions, not just those at the highest levels.

## CENTRE ON/REVOLVE AROUND

The key to using these phrases correctly is to think about their literal meaning. For example, you centre *on* (not around) a goal, just as you would centre on a target with a gun or bow and arrow. Likewise, your hobbies revolve *around* your early interest in water sports, just as the planets revolve around the sun in our solar system. Examples:

- All her selling points in the proposal *centred on* the need for greater productivity in the factory.
- At the latest annual meeting, some stockholders argued that most of the company's recent projects *revolved around* the CEO's interest in attracting attention from the media.

## CITE/SITE/SIGHT

1. *Cite* is a verb meaning "to quote as an example, authority, or proof." It can also mean "to commend" or "to bring before a court of law" (as in receiving a traffic ticket).
2. *Site* usually is a noun that means "a particular location." It can also be a verb that means "to place at a location," as with a new school being sited by the town square, but this usage is not preferred. Instead use a more conventional verb, such as *built*.
3. *Sight* is a noun meaning "the act of seeing" or "something that is seen." Or it can be a verb meaning "to see or observe."

Examples:

- We *cited* a famous geologist in our report on the earthquake.
- Rene was *cited* during the ceremony for her exemplary service to the city of Sudbury.

- The officer will *cite* the party-goers for disturbing the peace.
- Although five possible dorm *sites* were considered last year, the university administrators decided to build [preferred over *site*] the dorm at a different location.
- The *sight* of the flock of whooping cranes excited the visitors.
- Yesterday we *sighted* five whooping cranes at the marsh.

## COLONS

Colons are quite common in technical writing because they are used with lists. Here are the three main ways they are used:

### As a Formal Break before a List

As mentioned in the Lists entry, you should place a colon immediately after the last word before a list. Examples:

- Our field study included the tasks listed below:
- In our field study we were asked to complete the following tasks:

Note that a complete clause precedes the colon. Avoid incomplete constructions such as "In our field study, we were asked to:"

### As a Formal Break before a Point of Clarification or Elaboration

Examples:

- They were interested in just one issue: quality.
- John loved the dish because of its main ingredient: salmon.

### As a Formal Break before a Series within a Sentence

There are two ways to lead into a series within a sentence. First, you can lead smoothly into the series without a break and thus without using a colon. Second, you can include a formal stop that does require a colon. Both options are shown on below.

- Next month I will attend meetings in four cities: Vancouver, Nanaimo, Kamloops, and Kelowna.
- Next month I will attend conferences in Vancouver, Nanaimo, Kamloops, and Kelowna.

# COMMAS

Many writers struggle with commas, and for good reason. First, the teaching of punctuation is approached in different, and sometimes contradictory, ways. Second, comma rules are subject to some interpretation. And third, problems with commas sometimes reflect more fundamental problems with sentence structure.

The best strategy is to memorize a few basic rules of comma use. This knowledge will give you confidence in your ability to handle the mechanics of editing. (If you need help understanding any grammatical terms used in the rules, like *compound sentence,* refer to the Sentence Structure entries in this appendix.)

## Commas in a Series

Use commas to separate words, phrases, and short clauses written in a series of three or more items. According to current usage, a comma always precedes the *and* that comes before the last item in a series. Examples:

- The samples contained grey sand, sandy clay, and silty sand.
- The meal included steak, potatoes, and peaches and cream.

In the second example, note that the *and* before the last item in the series (and thus the one that is punctuated) is the one that precedes *peaches*. The other *and*—the one that precedes *cream*—has no comma before it because it connects only two parts of the last element in the series.

## Commas in Compound Sentences

Use a comma before the conjunction that joins main clauses in a compound sentence. Example:

We finished drilling the well, and then we grouted the holes with concrete.

The comma is used here because it separates two complete clauses, each with its own subject and verb ("we finished" and "we grouted"). If the second *we* had been deleted, there would be only one clause containing one subject and two verbs ("we finished and grouted"), and thus no comma would be needed. Of course, be certain that you don't use this comma rule to string together intolerably long sentences. Divide long sentences when you can. (See the Sentence Structure entry.)

## Commas with Nonessential Modifiers

Set off nonessential modifiers with commas—either at the beginning, middle, or end of sentences. Nonessential modifiers are phrases that add more information to a sentence rather than greatly changing its meaning. When you speak, often there is a pause between this kind of modifier and the main part of the sentence, giving a clue that a comma break is needed. Examples:

- The report, which we submitted three weeks ago, indicated that the company would not be responsible for transporting hazardous wastes.
- The report that we submitted three weeks ago indicated that the company would not be responsible for transporting hazardous wastes.

The first example includes a nonessential modifier. It would be spoken with pauses and therefore uses separating commas. The second example includes an essential modifier. It would be spoken without pauses and therefore includes no separating commas.

## Commas with Adjectives in a Series

Use a comma to separate two or more adjectives that modify the same noun. To help you decide if adjectives modify the same noun, use this test: if you can reverse their position and still retain the same meaning, then the adjectives modify the same word and should be separated by a comma. Example:

Jason opened the two containers in a dry, well-lighted place.

## Commas with Introductory Elements

Use a comma after introductory phrases or clauses of about five words or more. Example:

After completing its topographic survey of the area, the crew returned to headquarters for the weekly project meeting.

Commas like the one after *area* help readers separate secondary or modifying points from the main idea, which of course should be in the main clause. Without these commas, it may be difficult to read the sentence properly.

## Commas in Lists

Use commas in lists that you wish to treat as complete sentences. (See the Lists entries for a complete discussion of use and punctuation of listings.)

## Commas in Dates, Titles, Etc.

Abide by the conventions of comma usage in punctuating dates, titles, geographic place names, and addresses. Examples:

- May 3, 2004, is the projected date of completion.
- John F. Dunwoody, P. Eng. has been hired to direct the project because he is a registered engineer.
- McDuff, Inc., has been selected.
- He listed Winnipeg, Manitoba, as his permanent residence.

   Note the need for commas after the year "2004," the designation "Inc.," the province name "Manitoba," and the title "P. Eng." (as there would be for Ph.D.).

## COMPLEMENT/COMPLIMENT

Both words can be nouns and verbs, and both have adjective forms (*complementary, complimentary*).

## Complement

This word is used as a noun to mean "that which has made something whole or complete," as a verb to mean "to make whole, to make complete," or as an adjective to mean "serving as a complement." You may find it easier to remember the word by recalling its mathematical definition: two complementary angles must always equal 90 degrees. Examples:

- (as noun): The *complement* of five technicians brought our crew strength up to 100 percent.
- (as verb): The firm in Australia *complemented* ours in that together we won a joint contract for work in both countries.
- (as adjective): Seeing the project manager and her secretary work so well together made clear their *complementary* relationship in getting office work done.

## Compliment

This word is used as a noun to mean "an act of praise, flattery, or admiration," as a verb to mean "to praise, to flatter," or as an adjective to mean "related to praise or flattery, or without charge." Examples:

- (as noun): He appreciated the verbal *compliments*, but he also hoped they would result in a substantial raise.

- (as verb): Howard *complimented* the crew for finishing the job on time and within budget.
- (as adjective): We were fortunate to receive several *complimentary* copies of the new software from the publisher.

## COMPOSE/COMPRISE

*Compose* means "to make up or be included in," whereas *comprise* means "to include or consist of." The easiest way to remember this relationship is to memorize one sentence:

> The parts *compose* the whole, but the whole *comprises* the parts.

One more point to remember: the common phrase "is comprised of" is a substandard, unacceptable replacement for "comprise" or "is composed of." Careful writers don't use it. Examples:

- Seven separate layers *compose* the soils that were uncovered at the site.
- The borings revealed a stratigraphy that *comprises* [not *is comprised of*] seven separate layers.

## CONSUL/COUNCIL/COUNSEL

These three words can be distinguished by meaning and, in part, by their use within a sentence.

**Consul:** A noun meaning an official of a country who is sent to represent that country's interests in a foreign land.

**Council:** A noun meaning an official group or committee.

**Counsel:** A noun meaning an adviser or advice given OR a verb meaning to provide advice.

Examples:

- (consul) The Brazilian *consul* met with consular officials from three other countries.
- (council) The Human Resources *Council* of our company recommended a new retirement plan to the company president.
- (counsel—as noun) After the tragedy, they received legal *counsel* from their family attorney and spiritual *counsel* from their minister.

- (counsel—as verb) As a communications specialist, Roberta helps to *counsel* employees who are involved in various types of disputes.

## *CONTINUOUS/CONTINUAL*

These words have close yet distinctly different meanings. *Continuous* and *continuously* should be used in reference to uninterrupted, unceasing activities. *Continual* and *continually* should be used with activities that are intermittent, or repeated at intervals. If you think your reader may not understand the difference, use synonyms that will be more clear—such as *uninterrupted* for *continuous* and *intermittent* for *continual*. Examples:

- Because it rained *continuously* from 10 a.m. until noon, we were unable to find even a minute of clear sky to move our equipment onto the property.
- We *continually* checked the water pressure for three days before the equipment arrived, while also using the time to set up tests.

## *CRITERION/CRITERIA*

Coming from the Latin language, *criterion* and *criteria* are the singular and plural forms of a word that means "rationale or reasons for selecting a person, place, thing, or idea." A common error is to use *criteria* as both a singular and plural form, but such misuse disregards a distinction recognized by many readers. Maintain the distinction in your writing. Examples:

- Among all the qualifications we established for the new position, the most important *criterion* for success is good communication skills.
- She had to satisfy many *criteria* before being accepted into the honorary society of her profession.

## *DATA/DATUM*

Coming from the Latin, the word *data* is the plural form of *datum*. Traditionalists in the engineering and scientific community still consider *data* a plural form in all cases. However, in recent years some writers have considered *data* a plural form in some cases, when it means "facts," and a singular form in other cases, when it means "information." This book suggests you maintain the traditional use of data as a plural form, unless you have good reason to do otherwise. Examples:

- These *data* show that there is a strong case for building the dam at the other location.
- This particular *datum* shows we need to reconsider recommendations put forth in the original report.

If you consider the traditional singular form—*datum*—to be awkward, use substitutes such as "This item in the data demonstrates our point" or "One of the data demonstrates our point." Singular subjects like *one* or *item* allow you to keep your original meaning without using the word *datum*.

## DEFINITE/DEFINITIVE

Although similar in meaning, these two words have slightly different contexts. *Definite* refers to that which is precise, explicit, or final. *Definitive* has the more restrictive meaning of "authoritative" or "final." Examples:

- It is now *definite* that he will be assigned to the London office for six months.
- He received the *definitive* study on the effect of the oil spill on the marine ecology.

## DISCRETE/DISCREET/DISCRETION

The adjective *discrete* suggests something that is separate, or something that is made up of many separate parts. The adjective *discreet* is associated with actions that require caution, modesty, or reserve. The noun *discretion* refers to the quality of being "discreet" or the freedom a person has to act on his or her own. Examples:

- The company orientation program includes a writing seminar, which is a *discrete* training unit offered for one full day.
- The orientation program includes five *discrete* units.
- As a member of the human resources staff, Sunita was *discreet* in her handling of personal information about employees.
- Every human resources employee was instructed to show *discretion* in handling personal information about employees.
- By starting a "flextime" program, the company will give employees a good deal of *discretion* in selecting the time to start and end their workday.

## DISINTERESTED/UNINTERESTED

These words have quite different meanings. *Disinterested* means "without prejudice or bias," whereas *uninterested* means "showing no interest." Examples:

- The agency sought a *disinterested* observer who had no stake in the outcome of the trial.
- They spent several days talking to officials from Iceland, but they still remain *uninterested* in performing work in that country.

## DUE TO/BECAUSE OF

Mixing these two phrases can also cause confusion. *Due to* is an adjective phrase meaning "attributable to." It usually follows a "to be" verb such as *is, was,* or *were*. It should not be used in place of prepositional phrases such as *because of, owing to,* or *as a result of*. Examples:

- The cracked walls were *due to* the lack of proper fill being used during construction.
- We won the contract *because of* [not *due to*] our thorough understanding of the request for proposal.

## EACH OTHER/ONE ANOTHER

*Each other* occurs in contexts that include only two persons, whereas *one another* occurs in contexts that include three or more persons. Examples:

- Shana and Katie worked closely with *each other* during the project.
- All six members of the team conversed with *one another* regularly through e-mail.

## E.G./I.E.

The abbreviation *e.g.* means "for example," whereas *i.e.* means "that is." These two Latin abbreviations are often confused. Thus many writers prefer to write them out, rather than risk confusion on the part of the reader. Examples:

- He visited many cities where his firm plans to open offices—e.g. [or, preferably, *for example*], Kansas City, New Orleans, and Seattle.
- A spot along the Zayante Fault was the earthquake's epicentre—i.e. [or, preferably, *that is*], the focal point for seismic activity.

## ENGLISH AS A SECOND LANGUAGE (ESL)

Technical writing challenges native English speakers and non-native speakers alike. The purpose of this section is to present a basic description of three grammatical forms: articles, prepositions, and verbs. These forms may require more intense consideration from international students when they complete technical writing assignments. Each issue is described using the ease-of-operation section from the memo in Figure 2–2 on page 26. The passage, descriptions, and charts work together to show how these grammar issues function collectively to create meaning.

## *Articles*

Articles are one of the most difficult forms of English grammar for non-native English speakers, mainly because some language systems do not use them. Thus, speakers of particular languages may have to work hard to incorporate the English article system into their language proficiency.

The English articles include *a, an,* and *the.*

- *A* and *an* express indefinite meaning when they refer to nouns or pronouns or pronouns that are not specific. The writer believes the reader does not know the noun or pronoun.
- *The* expresses definite meaning when it refers to a specific noun or pronoun. The writer believes the reader knows the specific noun or pronoun.

*Ease of Operation—Article Usage*

**The** AIM 500 is so easy to operate that **a** novice can learn to transmit **a** document to another location in about two minutes. Here's **the** basic procedure:

1. Press **the** button marked TEL on **the** face of **the** fax machine. You then hear **a** dial tone.
2. Press **the** telephone number of **the** person receiving **the** fax on **the** number pad on **the** face of **the** machine.
3. Lay **the** document facedown on **the** tray at **the** back of **the** machine.

At this point, just wait for **the** document to be transmitted—about 18 seconds per page to transmit. **The** fax machine will even signal **the** user with **a** beep and **a** message on its LCD display when **the** document has been transmitted. Other more advanced operations are equally simple to use and require little training. Provided with **the** machine are two different charts that illustrate **the** machine's main functions.

**The** size of **the** AIM 500 makes it easy to set up almost anywhere in **an** office. **The** dimensions are 33 cm in width, 38 cm in length, and 24 cm in height. **The** narrow width, in particular, allows **the** machine to fit on most desks, file cabinets, or shelves.

ESL writers choose the correct article only when they (1) know the context or meaning, (2) determine whether they share information about the noun with the reader, and (3) consider the type of noun following the article.

The ease-of-operation passage includes 32 articles that represent two types—definite and indefinite. When a writer and a reader share knowledge of a noun, the definite article should be used. On 26 occasions the articles in the passage suggest the writer and reader share some knowledge of a count noun. Count nouns are nouns that can be counted (pen, cloud, memo). Examples of noncount nouns are *sugar, air,* and *beef.*

For example, the memo writer and the memo recipient share knowledge of the particular model fax machine—the AIM 500. Thus, "the" is definite when it refers to "the fax machine" in the memo. Notice, however, that "document"

### Articles from "Ease of Operation" Excerpt

| Article | Noun | Type | Comment |
|---------|------|------|---------|
| The | AIM 500 | definite | first mention—shared knowledge |
| a | novice | indefinite | first mention—no shared knowledge |
| a | document | indefinite | first mention—no shared knowledge |
| the | basic procedure | definite | |
| the | button | definite | |
| the | face | definite | |
| the | fax machine | definite | first mention without proper name, with reader/writer shared knowledge |
| a | dial tone | indefinite | first mention—no shared knowledge |
| the | telephone number | definite | |
| the | person | definite | |
| the | fax | definite | |
| the | number pad | definite | |
| the | face | definite | |
| the | machine | definite | |
| the | document | definite | |
| the | tray | definite | |
| the | back | definite | |
| the | machine | definite | |
| the | document | definite | second mention |
| The | fax machine | definite | |
| the | user | definite | |
| a | beep | indefinite | first mention—no shared knowledge |
| a | message | indefinite | first mention—no shared knowledge |
| the | document | definite | |
| the | machine | definite | |
| the | machine's main functions | definite | |
| The | size | definite | |
| the | AIM 500 | definite | |
| an | office | indefinite | first mention—preceding vowel sound—no shared knowledge |
| The | dimensions | definite | |
| The | narrow width | definite | |
| the | machine | definite | |

becomes definite only after the second time it is mentioned ("Lay the document facedown. . . ."). In the first reference to *document, a* document refers to a document about which the writer and reader share no knowledge. The memo writer cannot know which document the reader will fax. Only in the second reference do the writer and reader know the document to be the one the reader will fax.

The indefinite article *a* occurs five times, while *an* occurs once. Each occurrence signals a singular count noun. The reader and the writer share no knowledge of the nouns that follow the *a* or *an,* so an indefinite article is appropriate. *A* precedes nouns beginning with consonant sounds. *An* precedes nouns beginning with vowel sounds. Indefinite articles seldom precede noncount nouns unless a non-count functions as a modifier (a beef shortage).

Definite and indefinite articles are used more frequently than other articles; however, other articles do exist. The "generic" article refers to classes or groups of people, objects, and ideas. If the fax machine is thought of in a general sense, the meaning changes. For example, "the fax machine increased office productivity by 33 percent." *The* now has a generic meaning representing fax machines in general. The same generic meaning can apply to the plural noun, but such generic use requires no article. "Fax machines increased office productivity by 33 percent." *The* in this instance is a generic article.

## Verbs

Verbs express time in three ways—simple present, simple past, and future. *Wait, waited,* and *will wait* and *lay (to put), laid,* and *will lay* are examples of simple present, simple past, and future tense verbs. Unfortunately, the English verb system is more complicated than that. Verbs express more than time.

*Ease of Operation—Verb Usage*

The AIM 500 **is** so easy to operate that a novice **can learn** to transmit a document to another location in about two minutes. **Here's** the basic procedure:

1. **Press** the button marked TEL on the face of the fax machine. You then **hear** a dial tone.
2. **Press** the telephone number of the person receiving the fax on the number pad on the face of the machine.
3. **Lay** the document facedown on the tray at the back of the machine.

At this point, just **wait** for the document to be transmitted—about 18 seconds per page to transmit. The fax machine **will** even **signal** the user with a beep and a message on its LCD display when the document **has been transmitted.** Other more advanced operations **are** equally simple to use

## Regular Verbs

| Present | Past | Future |
|---|---|---|
| learn | learned | will learn |
| wait | waited | will wait |
| press | pressed | will press |
| signal | signaled | will signal |
| require | required | will require |
| provide | provided | will provide |
| illustrate | illustrated | will illustrate |
| allow | allowed | will allow |
| **present perfect** | **past perfect** | **future perfect** |
| have learned | had learned | will have learned |
| have waited | had waited | will have waited |
| have pressed | had pressed | will have pressed |
| have signaled | had signaled | will have signaled |
| have required | had required | will have required |
| have provided | had provided | will have provided |
| have illustrated | had illustrated | will have illustrated |
| have allowed | had allowed | will have allowed |

and **require** little training. **Provided** with the machine **are** two different charts that **illustrate** the machine's main functions.

The size of the AIM 500 **makes** it easy to set up almost anywhere in an office. The dimensions **are** 33 cm in width, 38 cm in length, and 24 cm in height. The narrow width, in particular, **allows** the machine to fit on most desks, file cabinets, or shelves.

Verbs in the English language system appear either as regular or irregular forms. Regular verbs follow a predictable pattern.

- The form of the simple present tense verbs *(walk)* changes to the simple past tense with the addition of *ed (walked)*.
- The past tense *walked* changes to the perfect tense with the addition of an auxiliary (helping) word to the simple past tense form. For example, "I have walked" is present perfect, and "I had walked" is past perfect.

Irregular verbs do not follow a predictable pattern.

- Most important, the past tense is not created by adding *ed*. The simple present tense of lay *(to put)* changes completely in the simple past *(laid)*.
- Like regular verbs, the past tense *(laid)* changes to the perfect tense with the addition of an auxiliary verb.

### Irregular Verbs

| Present | Past | Future |
|---|---|---|
| is | was | will be |
| are | were | will be |
| hear | heard | will hear |
| do | did | will do |
| get | got | will get |
| see | saw | will see |
| write | wrote | will write |
| speak | spoke | will speak |
| **present perfect** | **past perfect** | **future perfect** |
| have been (he, she, it) | had been | will have been |
| have been (they) | had been | will have been |
| have heard | had heard | will have heard |
| have done | had done | will have done |
| have gotten | had gotten | will have gotten |
| have seen | had seen | will have seen |
| have written | had written | will have written |
| have spoken | had spoken | will have spoken |

"I have laid the document facedown on the tray" is present perfect, and "I had laid the document facedown on the tray" is past perfect.

Let's examine four specific verb forms in the "Ease of Operation" passage.

1. *Is* represents a being or linking verb in the passage. Being verbs suggest an aspect of an experience or being (existence); for example, "He is still here," and "the fax is broken." Linking verbs connect a subject to a complement (completer); for example, "The fax machine is inexpensive."

2. *Can learn* is the present tense verb *learn* preceded by a modal. Modals assist verbs to convey meaning. *Can* suggests ability or possibility. Other modals and their meanings appear below.

| will | would | could | shall | should | might | must |
|---|---|---|---|---|---|---|
| scientific fact possibility determination | hypothetical | hypothetical | formal will | expectation obligation | possibility | necessity |

3. *Here's* shows a linking verb *(is)* connected to its complement *(here)*. The sentence in its usual order—subject first followed by the verb—would

appear as, "The basic procedure is here" (article—adjective—noun—linking verb—complement).

4. *Press, Lay,* and *wait* (for) share at least four common traits: present tense, singular number, action to transitive, and understood subject of *you*. Although *you* does not appear in the text, the procedure clearly instructs the person operating the fax machine—*you*. Action or transitive verbs express movement, activity, and momentum, and may take objects. Objects answer the questions who? what? to whom? or for whom? in relation to transitive verbs. For example, "Press the button." "Hear a dial tone." "Press the telephone number." "Lay the document facedown." Press what? Hear what? Lay what?

### Verbs from "Ease of Operation" Excerpt

| Verb | Tense | Number | Other details |
|---|---|---|---|
| is | present | singular | linking/being (is, was, been) |
| can learn | present | singular | *can* is a modal auxiliary implying "possibility" |
| here's (is) | present | singular | linking/being |
| Press | present | singular | understood *you* as subject |
| hear | present | singular | action/transitive |
| Press | present | singular | understood *you* as subject |
| Lay | present | singular | irregular (lay, laid, laid) singular—understood *you* as subject |
| wait | present | singular | understood *you* as subject |
| will signal | future | singular | action to happen or condition to experience—understood *you* as subject |
| has been transmitted | present perfect | singular | passive voice—action that began in the past and continues to the present |
| are | present | plural | linking/being |
| require | present | plural | action/transitive |
| Provided are | present perfect | plural | passive voice—action that began in the past and continues to the present |
| illustrate | present | plural | action/transitive |
| makes | present | singular | action/transitive |
| are | present | plural | linking/being |
| allows | present | singular | action/transitive |

## Prepositions

Prepositions are words that become a part of a phrase composed of the preposition, a noun or pronoun, and any modifiers.

*Ease of Operation—Preposition Usage*

The AIM 500 is so easy to operate that a novice can learn to transmit a document **to** another location **in** about two minutes. Here's the basic procedure:

1. Press the button marked TEL **on** the face **of** the fax machine. You then hear a dial tone.
2. Press the telephone number **of** the person receiving the fax **on** the number pad **on** the face **of** the machine.
3. Lay the document facedown **on** the tray **at** the back **of** the machine.

   **At** this point, just wait **for** the document to be transmitted—**about** 18 seconds **per** page to transmit. The fax machine will even signal the user **with** a beep and a message **on** its LCD display when the document has been transmitted. Other more advanced operations are equally simple to use and require little training. Provided **with** the machine are two different charts that illustrate the machine's main functions.

   The size **of** the AIM 500 makes it easy to set up almost anywhere **in** an office. The dimensions are 33 cm **in** width, 38 cm **in** length, and 24 cm **in** height. The narrow width, **in** particular, allows the machine to fit **on** most desks, file cabinets, or shelves.

Notice the relationships expressed within the prepositional phrases and the ways they affect meaning in the sentences. In the "Ease of Operation" passage, about half the prepositional phrases function as adverbs noting place or time. The other half function as adjectives.

| Place          or | Location | Time |
|---|---|---|
| at | above | after |
| below | around | before |
| beneath | inside | during |
| in | near | since |
| into | on | |
| outside | out | |
| over | under | |
| within | underneath | |

   One important exception is a preposition that connects to a verb to make a "prepositional" verb, *wait for.* Another interesting quality of prepositions is that sometimes more than one can be used to express similar meaning. In the "Ease of Operation" passage, for example, both *on* the tray and *at* the back indicate position. Another way to state the same information is *on* the tray *on* the back.

### Prepositions from "Ease of Operation" Excerpt

| Preposition | Noun Phrase | Comment |
|---|---|---|
| to | another location | direction toward |
| in | (about) two minutes | approximation of time |
| on | the face | position |
| of | the fax machine | originating at or from |
| of | the person | associated with |
| on | the number | position |
| on | the face | position |
| of | the machine | originating at |
| on | the tray | position |
| at | the back | position of |
| of | the machine | originating at |
| At | this point | on or near the time |
| for | the document | indication of object of desire |
| about | 18 seconds | adverb = approximation |
| per | page | for every |
| with | a beep and a message | accompanying |
| on | its LCD display | position |
| with | the machine | accompanying |
| of | the AIM 500 | originating at or from |
| in | an office | within the area |
| in | width | with reference to |
| in | length | with reference to |
| in | height | with reference to |
| in | particular | with reference to |
| on | most desks, file cabinets, or shelves | position |

## FARTHER/FURTHER

Although similar in meaning, these two words are used differently. *Farther* refers to actual physical distance, whereas *further* refers to nonphysical distance or can mean "additional." Examples:

- The overhead projector was moved *farther* from the screen so that the print would be easier to see.
- *Farther* up the old lumber road, they found footprints of an unidentified mammal.

- As he read *further* along in the report, he began to understand the complexity of the project.
- She gave *further* instructions after they arrived at the site.

## FEWER/LESS

The adjective *fewer* is used before items that can be counted, whereas the adjective *less* is used before mass quantities. When errors occur, they usually result from *less* being used with countable items, as in this *incorrect* sentence: "We can complete the job with less men at the site." Examples:

- "The newly certified industrial hygienist signed with us because the other firm in which he was interested offered *fewer* [not *less*] benefits."
- "There was *less* sand in the sample taken from 4.5 m than in the one taken from 3m."

## FLAMMABLE/INFLAMMABLE/NONFLAMMABLE

Given the importance of these words in avoiding injury and death, make sure to use them correctly—especially in instructions.

1. *Flammable* means "capable of burning quickly" and is accepted usage.
2. *Inflammable* has the same meaning as *flammable*. However, it is *not* acceptable usage because readers may confuse it with *nonflammable*.
3. *Nonflammable* means "not capable of burning" and is accepted usage.

Examples:

- They marked the package *flammable* because its contents could be easily ignited by a spark. [Note that *flammable* is preferred here over its synonym, *inflammable*.]
- The supervisor was not worried about placing the crates near the heating unit, because all the contents were *nonflammable*.

## FORMER/LATTER

These two words direct the reader's attention to previous points or items. *Former* refers to that which came first, whereas *latter* refers to that which came last. Note that the words are used together only with *two* items or points—*not* with three or more. Also, you should know that some readers may prefer you avoid *former* and *latter* altogether, for the construction may force them to look back to previous sentences to understand your meaning. The second example below gives an alternative.

- (with former/latter) The airline's machinists and flight attendants went on strike yesterday. The *former* left work in the morning, whereas the *latter* left work in the afternoon.
- (without former/latter) The airline's machinists and flight attendants went on strike yesterday. The machinists left work in the morning, whereas the flight attendants left work in the afternoon.

## *FORTUITOUS/FORTUNATE*

The adjective *fortuitous* indicates an action is unexpected, whether it is desirable or not. The adjective *fortunate* indicates an action is desired. A common error is the wrong assumption that "fortuitous" events must also be "fortunate." Examples:

- Seeing M&K's London manager at the conference was quite *fortuitous*, for I had not been told that he also was attending.
- It was indeed *fortunate* that I encountered the Tokyo manager, for we had the chance to talk about a project involving both our offices.

## *GENERALLY/TYPICALLY/USUALLY*

Words like these can be useful qualifiers in your reports. All three indicate that something is often, but not always, true. Place these adverb modifiers as close as possible to the words they modify. For example, in the first example below it would be inaccurate to write "were typically sampled," because "typically" modifies the entire verb phrase "were sampled." Examples:

- Cohesionless soils *typically* were sampled by driving a 5 cm diameter, split-barrel sampler. (Active-voice alternative: *Typically*, we sampled cohesionless soils by driving a 5 cm diameter, split-barrel sampler.)
- For projects like the one you propose, *usually* the technician will clean the equipment before returning to the office.
- It *generally* is known that sites for dumping waste should be equipped with appropriate liners.

## GOOD/WELL

Although these words have similar meanings, *good* is used as an adjective, and *well* is used as an adverb. A common usage error occurs when writers use the adjective when the adverb is required. Examples:

- It is *good* practice to submit three-year plans on time.
- Although he had a slight case of the flu, he felt *well* enough to attend the seminar.

## HOPEFULLY

Use and abuse of this adverb have attracted far more attention than it probably deserves. Yet you should know that some readers will make judgments about your level of literacy by your ability to use *hopefully* correctly. Use the word correctly to avoid drawing attention away from the content of your writing.

*Hopefully* is an adverb that means "with hope," *not* a one-word substitute for "I hope that." In other words, use *hopefully* only when it serves as an adverb and explicitly means "with hope." Examples:

- I looked *hopefully* through the files for the client's lost report. [That is, I looked "with hope."]
- They waited *hopefully* for the results of the proposal competition. [That is, they waited "with hope."]
- *I hope* I'll find the report before my client arrives for the meeting. [Not "Hopefully, I'll find . . . "]
- *They hoped* their firm would win the proposal competition. [Not "Hopefully, their firm would win . . . "]

## IMPLY/INFER

The person doing the speaking or writing "implies." The person hearing or reading the words "infers." Thus the word *imply* requires an active role, whereas the word *infer* requires a passive role. When you imply a point, your words suggest rather than state a point. When you infer a point, you form a conclusion or deduce meaning from someone else's words. Examples:

- The contracts officer *implied* that there would be stiff competition for that $20 million waste treatment project.
- We *inferred* from her remarks that the firm selected for the work must have completed similar projects recently.

## ITS/IT'S

These words are often confused. *It's* with the apostrophe is *only* used as a contraction for "it is" or "it has." The other form—*its*—is a possessive pronoun. (*Its'* is not a word.) Examples:

- Because of the rain, *it's* [or *it is*] going to be difficult to move the equipment to the site.
- *It's* [or *it has*] been a long time since we submitted the proposal.
- The company completed *its* part of the agreement on time.

## LAY/LIE

These two verbs are troublesome, and you need to know some basic grammar to use them correctly.

1. *Lay* means "to place." It is a transitive verb; thus it takes a direct object to which it conveys action. ("She laid down the printout before starting the meeting.") Its main forms are *lay* (present), *laid* (past), *laid* (past participle), and *laying* (present participle).
2. *Lie* means "to be in a reclining position." It is an intransitive verb; thus it does not take a direct object. ("In some countries, it is acceptable for workers to lie down for a midday nap.") Its main forms are *lie* (present), *lay* (past), *lain* (past participle), and *lying* (present participle).

If you want to use these words with confidence, remember the transitive/intransitive distinction and memorize the principal parts. Examples:

- (lay) I will *lay* the notebook on the lab desk before noon.
- (lay) I have *laid* the notebook there before.
- (lay) I was *laying* the notebook down when the phone rang.
- (lie) The watchdog *lies* motionless at the warehouse gate.
- (lie) The dog *lay* there yesterday too.
- (lie) The dog has *lain* there for three hours today and no doubt will be *lying* there when I return from lunch.

## LEAD/LED

*Lead* is either a noun that names the metallic element or a verb that means "to direct or show the way." *Led* is only a verb form, the past tense of the verb *lead*. Examples:

- The company bought rights to mine *lead* on the land.
- They chose a new president to *lead* the firm into the twenty-first century.
- They were *led* to believe that salary raises would be high this year.

## LETTER FORMATS

Many organizations adopt letter formats used uniformly by all employees. Other organizations permit flexibility. In the latter case, you have three basic formats from which to choose—(1) block (with or without indented paragraphs), (2) modified block, or (3) simplified. Figures B–1, B–2, and B–3 on the next three pages provide guidelines for each format.

## LIKE/AS

These two words are different parts of speech and thus are used differently in sentences. *Like* is a preposition and therefore is followed by an object—not an entire clause. *As* is a conjunction and thus is followed by a group of words that include a verb. *As if* and *as though* are related conjunctions. Examples:

- Gary looks *like* his father.
- Managers *like* John will be promoted quickly.
- If Teresa writes this report *as* she wrote the last one, our clients will be pleased.
- Our proposals are brief, *as* they should be.
- Our branch manager talks *as though* [or *as if*] the merger will take place soon.

## LISTS: GENERAL POINTERS

Lists draw attention to three or more pieces of like information that are important enough to be set apart from standard text format. In other words, they are an attention-getting strategy. Following are some general pointers for using lists:

### Strive for a Range of from Three to Nine Items

Most readers hold up to nine items in short-term memory. More than nine items gives the appearance of a disorganized "laundry list"; it may confuse

Letterhead of your organization

Two or more blank lines (adjust space to centre letter on page)

Date of letter

Two or more blank lines (adjust space to centre letter on page)

Address of reader

One blank line

Greeting

One blank line

Paragraph: single-spaced (indenting optional)

One blank line

Paragraph: single-spaced (indenting optional)

One blank line

Paragraph: single-spaced (indenting optional)

One blank line

Complimentary close

Three blank lines (for signature)

Typed name and title

One blank line

Typist's initials (optional: Writer's initials before typist's initials)

Computer file # (if applicable)

One blank line (optional)

Enclosure notation

One blank line (optional)

Copy notation

**FIGURE B–1**
Letter format: Block
(adapted *Technical Writing* 3/c/e p. 211).

Letterhead of your organization

Two or more blank lines (adjust space to centre letter on page)

Date of letter

Two or more blank lines (adjust space to centre letter on page)

Address of reader

One blank line

Greeting

One blank line

Paragraph: single-spaced, with first line indented 5 spaces

One blank line

Paragraph: single-spaced, with first line indented 5 spaces

One blank line

Paragraph: single-spaced, with first line indented 5 spaces

One blank line

Complimentary close

Three blank lines (for signature)

Typed name and title

One blank line

Typist's initials (optional: Writer's initials before typist's initials)

Computer file # (if applicable)

One blank line (optional)

Enclosure notation

One blank line (optional)

Copy notation

**FIGURE B–2**
Letter format: Modified block
(adapted *Technical Writing* 3/c/e p. 212).

Letterhead of organization

Two or more blank lines (adjust space to centre letter on page)

Date of letter

Two or more blank lines (adjust space to centre letter on page)

Address of reader

Three blank lines

Short subject line

Three blank lines

Paragraph: single-spaced, no indenting

One blank line

Paragraph: single-spaced, no indenting

One blank line

Paragraph: single-spaced, no indenting

Five blank lines (for signature)

Typed name and title

One blank line (optional)

Typist's initials (optional: Writer's initials before typist's initials)

Computer file # (if applicable)

One blank line (optional)

Enclosure notation

One blank line (optional)

Copy notation

**FIGURE B–3**
Letter format: Simplified
(adapted *Technical Writing* 3/c/e p. 213).

rather than clarify an issue. If you have more than nine items, consider grouping them in three or four categories, as you would in an outline. Groups make it easier for readers to grasp and remember many points.

## Use Bullets (•) for Groupings That Do Not Involve Sequence

The single round bullets are best. Avoid strange-shaped bullets that draw more attention to themselves than to your ideas.

## Use Numbers to Convey Sequence

Numbers work best when you are listing ordered items such as steps, procedures, or ranked alternatives.

## Keep Points Parallel

*Parallel* means that all points in the same list are in the same grammatical form—whether a complete sentence, verb phrase, or noun phrase. If you change form in the middle of a listing, you risk upsetting the flow of your text. Example:

> To complete this project, we planned the following tasks:
> - Survey the site
> - Take samples from the three boring locations
> - Test selected samples in our lab
> - Report on the results of the study

The items above are in verb form (note introductory words *survey, take, test, report*). An alternative would be to put them in noun form, with a different lead-in.

## LISTS: PUNCTUATION

You have three main options for punctuating lists. In all three you should (1) precede the list with a lead-in that is a complete thought, as in the preceding example, (2) place a colon after the last word of the lead-in, and (3) capitalize the first letter of the first word of each listed item.

## Option A: Place No Punctuation after Listed Items

This style is particularly appropriate when a list includes only short phrases. More and more writers are choosing this option. Example:

In this study we will develop recommendations that address the following concerns in your project:

- Site preparation
- Foundation design
- Sanitary sewer design
- Storm sewer design
- Geologic surface faulting
- Projections for regional land subsidence

## *Option B: Treat the List like a Sentence Series*

In this case you place commas or semicolons between items and a period at the end of the series. Whether you choose Option A or B largely depends on your own style. Example:

In this study we developed recommendations that dealt with four topics:

- Site preparation,
- Foundation design,
- Sewer construction, and
- Geologic faulting.

This option requires that you place an *and* after the comma that appears before the last item. Another variation of Option B occurs when you have internal commas within one or more of the items. In this case, you need to change the commas that follow the listed items into semicolons. Yet you still keep the *and* before the last item. Example:

Last month we completed environmental assessments at three sites:

- A gas refinery in Calgary, Alberta;
- A chemical plant in Sudbury, Ontario; and
- A waste pit outside of Baton Rouge, Louisiana.

## *Option C: Treat Each Item like a Separate Sentence*

When items in a list are complete sentences, you can punctuate each one as a separate sentence, placing a period at the end of each. Example:

The main conclusions of our preliminary assessment are summarized here:

- At five of the six borehole locations, petroleum hydrocarbons were detected at concentrations greater than a background concentration of 10 mg/kg.
- No PCB concentrations were detected in the subsurface soils we analyzed. We will continue the testing, as outlined in our proposal.

- Sampling and testing should be restarted three weeks from the date of this report.

## LOOSE/LOSE

*Loose,* which rhymes with *goose,* is an adjective that means "unfastened, flexible, or unconfined." *Lose,* which rhymes with *choose,* is a verb that means to "misplace." Examples:

- The power failure was linked to a *loose* connection at the switchbox.
- Because of poor service, the copying machine company may *lose* its contract with our San Francisco office.

## MEMO FORMAT

With minor variations, most memoranda (memos) look much the same. The "date/to/from/subject" information hangs at the top left margin, in whatever order your organization requires. These lines help you avoid lengthy introductory information in the memo itself. Figure B–4 on the next page outlines the format for a typical memo. Pay special attention to the "subject" line, for it immediately conveys the meaning of the memo to readers. In fact, readers use it to decide when, or if, they will read the complete memo. Be brief, but engage interest.

## MODIFIERS

Words, phrases, and even dependent clauses can serve as modifiers in a sentence. Their purpose is to qualify, or add meaning to, other elements in the sentence.

Modifiers need to be clearly connected to what they modify. When the connection is not clear, modification errors can occur. Such errors occur most often with phrases that include verbals. There are three types of verbals:

1. **Gerunds:** Nouns that are formed by adding *-ing* to a verb form—for example, "Skiing is his favourite hobby."
2. **Participles:** Adjectives that are formed by adding *-ing* or *-ed* to a verb form—for example, "John is very particular about his writing utensils."

| Facsimile reference |
| One or more blank lines |

| Date of memo |
| Reader's name (and position, if appropriate) |
| Writer's name (and position, if appropriate) |
| Subject of memo |
| One or more blank lines |

| Paragraph: Single-spaced (optional—first line indented) |
| One blank line |

| Paragraph: Single-spaced (optional—first line indented) |
| One blank line |

| Paragraph: Single-spaced (optional—first line indented) |
| One blank line |

| Typist's initials (optional—writer's initials before typist's initials) |
| One blank line |

| Enclosure notation |
| One blank line |

| Copy notation |

**FIGURE B–4**
Memorandum format
(adapted *Technical Writing* 3/c/e p. 188).

3. **Infinitives:** A phrase that includes the word *to* and a verb root—for example, "To attend college was his main goal."

Modification errors can occur with all verbals. However, they are most common with participles and come in the form of dangling or misplaced modifiers.

## *Dangling Modifiers*

When a verbal phrase "dangles," the sentence in which it is used contains no specific word for the phrase to modify. As a result, the meaning of the sentence can be confusing to the reader. You can correct dangling modifiers either by (1) rewording the sentence to give the participle a specific noun to modify (see Revision 1) or by (2) recasting the sentence to remove the participle (see Revision 2).

**Original:** Using an angle of friction of 20 degrees and a vertical weight of 300 tonnes, the sliding resistance would be as shown on Table 2.

**Revision 1:** Using an angle of friction of 20 degrees and a vertical weight of 300 tonnes, we computed a sliding resistance as shown on Table 2.

**Revision 2:** If the angle of friction is 20 degrees and the vertical weight is 300 tonnes, the sliding resistance should be as shown on Table 2.

## Misplaced Modifiers

When a verbal phrase is misplaced, it appears to refer to a word that it does not modify. At best, misplaced modifiers can lead to unintentionally amusing prose. At worst, they can cause confusion about the agent of action in technical tasks. Correct the error by recasting the sentence, with modifiers clearly connected to what they modify.

**Original:** Floating peacefully near the oil rig, we saw two humpback whales. [The sentence should indicate the whales are floating.]

**Revision:** We saw two humpback whales floating peacefully near the oil rig.

**Original:** Before beginning to dig the observation trenches, we recommend that the contractors submit their proposed excavation program for our review.

**Revision:** We recommend the following: before the contractors begin digging observation trenches, they should submit their proposed excavation program for our review.

## NUMBERS

Like rules for abbreviations, those for numbers may vary from profession to profession and even from company to company. Most technical writing subscribes to the approach that numbers are best expressed in figures (45) rather than words (forty-five). Note that this style may differ from that in other types of writing. Unless the preferences of a particular reader suggest you do otherwise, use the following common rules for numbers:

## Follow the 10-or-over Rule

In general, use figures for numbers of 10 or more, words for numbers below 10. Examples:

> Three technicians at the site; 15 reports submitted last month; one rig contracted for the job

## Do Not Start Sentences with Figures

Begin sentences with the word form of numbers, not with figures. Example:

> Forty-five containers were shipped back to the lab.

## Use Figures as Modifiers

Whether above or below 10, numbers are usually expressed as figures when used as modifiers with units of measurement, time, and money. Examples:

> 4 cm, 7 hr, 17 mL, $5 per hour

## Use Figures in a Group of Mixed Numbers

Use only figures when the numbers grouped together in a passage (usually just one sentence) are both above and below 10. Example:

> For that project they assembled 15 samplers, 4 rigs, and 25 large containers.

In other words, this rule argues for consistency within a writing unit.

## Use the Figure Form in Illustration Titles

Use the figure (numeric) form when labelling specific tables and figures in your reports. Example:

> Figure 3, Table 14–B

## Be Careful with Fractions

Express fractions as words when they stand alone, but as figures when they are used as a modifier or are joined to whole numbers. Example:

> We have completed two-thirds of the project using the 2½-in. pipe.

## *Use Figures and Words with Numbers in Succession*

When two numbers appear in succession in the same unit, write the first as a word and the second as a figure. Example:

> We found fifteen 2 m pieces of pipe in the bin.

## *Only Rarely Use Numbers in Parentheses*

Except in legal documents, avoid the practice of placing figures in parentheses after their word equivalents. Example:

> The second party will pay the first party forty-five (45) dollars on or before the first of each month.

Note that the parenthetical amount is placed immediately after the figure, not after the unit of measurement.

## *Use Figures with Dollars*

Use figures with all dollar amounts, with the exception of the context noted in the preceding rule. Avoid cents columns unless exactness to the penny is necessary.

## *Use Commas in Four-Digit Figures*

To prevent possible misreading, use commas in figures of four digits or more. Example:

> 15,000; 1,247; 6,003

## *Use Words for Ordinals*

Usually spell out the ordinal form of numbers. Example:

> The judge informed the first, second, and third choices [not *1st, 2nd,* and *3rd* choices] in the design competition.

A notable exception is graphics, where space limitations could argue for use of the abbreviated form.

---

## *NUMBER OF/TOTAL OF*

These two phrases can take singular or plural verbs, depending on the context. Here are two simple rules for correct usage:

1. If the phrase is preceded by *the,* it takes a singular verb because emphasis is placed on the group.
2. If the phrase is preceded by *a,* it takes a plural verb because emphasis is placed on the many individual items.

Examples:

- *The number of* projects going over budget *has* decreased dramatically.
- *The total of* 90 lawyers *believes* the courtroom guidelines should be changed.
- *A number* of projects *have* stayed within budget recently.
- *A total of* 90 lawyers *believe* the courtroom guidelines should be changed.

## *ORAL/VERBAL*

*Oral* refers to words that are spoken, as in *"oral presentation." Verbal* refers to spoken or written language, as opposed to "nonverbal" communication such as body language. Avoid the common error of using *verbal* as a substitute for *oral.* Examples:

- In its international operations, our firm has learned that some countries still rely on *oral* [not *verbal*] contracts.
- Their *oral* [not *verbal*] agreement last month was followed by a *written* [not *verbal*] contract this month.

## *PARAGRAPH GUIDELINES*

Paragraphs have two objectives. First, they must state and then develop a topic. Second, they must maintain reader interest in the main idea. These objectives sometimes seem to work at cross-purposes, for many writers force paragraphs to bear the burden of too much detail. Remember that readers become frustrated by (and even tend to skip over) paragraphs that go beyond six or eight lines.

Here are five rules to help you write clear, thoughtful, and engaging paragraphs:

### *Put the Main Point First*

Start the paragraph with your main idea. Do not delay or bury the main point in the middle of the paragraph. Readers who skim documents will usually focus on the first sentences of paragraphs. If you fail to put the main point there, they may miss your point entirely.

## Keep Paragraphs Short

Restrict paragraph length to six or eight lines. Most people do not want to read more than that without a visual break. If your idea requires more thorough treatment, divide the topic at a convenient point and use two paragraphs to develop it.

## Use Lists

Take groups of related points and form bulleted or numbered lists within the paragraph. Readers lose patience when information could have been more clearly presented in listings.

## Avoid Extensive Use of Numbers

Paragraphs are the worst format for presenting data of any kind, especially numbers that describe costs. Readers may ignore or miss data that are packed into paragraphs. Usually tables or figures would be a clearer and more appropriate format. Also, be aware that some readers may think that cost data couched in paragraph form represent an attempt to hide important information.

## Give Readers Some Variety

Alter the length of paragraphs, to make your writing more visually appealing. Remember that a very short paragraph should emphasize a major point or provide a transition between two longer paragraphs.

## PARENTHESES

Use parentheses sparingly because long parenthetical expressions can distract readers. But they are useful for enclosing the following items:

- An abbreviation immediately following the complete term
- A brief explanation that provides extra, subordinate information
- Reference citations within the text

As for punctuation, a period goes after the close parenthesis when the parenthetical information is part of the sentence (as in this sentence).

(However, the period goes inside the close parenthesis when the parenthetical information forms its own sentence, as in the sentence you are reading.)

## PARTS OF SPEECH

This term refers to the eight main groups of words in English grammar. A word's placement into one of these groups is based upon its function within the sentence, as described here:

### Nouns

Nouns name persons, places, objects, or ideas. The two major categories are (1) proper nouns and (2) common nouns. Proper nouns name specific persons, places, objects, or ideas, and they are capitalized. Examples:

> Toronto, St. Lawrence River, Apple Computer, Student Government Association, Susan Jones, Enlightenment

Common nouns name general groups of persons, places, objects, and ideas, and they are not capitalized. Examples:

> trucks, farmers, engineers, assembly lines, philosophy, committee

### Verbs

Verbs express action or state of being. As such they give movement to the sentence and form the core of meaning in your writing. Examples:

> explore, grasp, write, develop, is, has

### Pronouns

Pronouns act as substitutes for nouns. Some sample pronoun categories include the following:

- Personal pronouns (I, we, you, she, he)
- Relative pronouns (who, whom, that, which)
- Reflexive and intensive pronouns (myself, yourself, itself)
- Demonstrative pronouns (this, that, these, those)
- Indefinite pronouns (all, any, each, anyone)

## *Adjectives*

Adjectives modify nouns and thus add meaning to them. Examples:

> horizontal, stationary, green, large, simple

## *Adverbs*

Adverbs modify verbs, adjectives, other adverbs, or whole statements. Examples:

> soon, generally, well, very, too, greatly

## *Prepositions*

Prepositions show the relationship between nouns or pronouns (called the objects of prepositions) and other elements in a sentence. Forming a prepositional phrase, the preposition and its object can reveal relationships such as location, time, and direction. Examples:

- They went *over the hill.* (location)
- He left *after the meeting.* (time)
- She walked *toward the office.* (direction)

## *Conjunctions*

Conjunctions are connecting words that link words, phrases, or clauses. They are called coordinate conjunctions when they link like elements, such as two main clauses. They are called subordinate conjunctions when they link two different elements, such as a dependent clause and an independent clause. Examples:

- Coordinate: and, but, for, nor, or, so, yet
- Subordinate: after, although, as if, because, before, even though, if, now that, once, since, so that, though, unless, until, when, whenever, where, whereas, while

## *Interjections*

As an expression of emotion, these words can stand alone (Look out!), or they can be inserted into another sentence (*Oh*, now I understand what you meant in your proposal).

## PASSED/PAST

*Passed* is the past tense of the verb *pass,* whereas *past* is an adjective, preposition, or noun that means "previous" or "beyond" or "a time before the present." Examples:

- He *passed* the survey marker on his way to the construction site.
- The *past* president attended last night's meeting. [adjective]
- He worked *past* midnight on the project. [preposition]
- In the distant *past,* the valley was a tribal hunting ground. [noun]

## PER

Coming from the Latin, this word should be reserved for business and technical expressions that involve statistics or measurement—such as "per annum" or "per kilometre." It should *not* be used as a stuffy substitute for "in accordance with." Examples:

- Her *per diem* travel allowance of $90 covered hotels and meals.
- During the oil crisis years ago, gasoline prices increased by over 50 cents *per gallon.*
- *As you requested* [not *per your request*], we have enclosed brochures on our products.

## PER CENT/PERCENT/PERCENTAGE

*Per cent* and *percent* have basically the same usage and occur with exact numbers. The one word *percent* is preferred. Even more common in technical writing, however, is the use of the percentage sign (%) after numbers. The word *percentage* is used only to express general amounts, not exact numbers. Examples:

- After completing a marketing survey, we discovered that 83 *percent* [or 83%] of our current clients have hired us for previous projects.
- A large *percentage* of the defects can be linked to the loss of two experienced inspectors.

## PRACTICAL/PRACTICABLE

Although close in meaning, these two words have quite different implications. *Practical* refers to an action that is known to be effective. *Practicable* refers to an action that can be accomplished or put into practice, without regard for its effectiveness or practicality. Examples:

- His *practical* solution to the underemployment problem led to a 30% increase in employment last year.
- The department head presented a *practicable* response, for it already had been put into practice in another branch.

## PRINCIPAL/PRINCIPLE

When these two words are misused, the careful reader will notice. After reading the sections that follow, you will understand why "The principal principle maintained by the principals of the bank is the importance of both interest and principal."

### *Principal*

*Principal* can be either a noun or adjective and has three basic uses:

1. As a noun meaning "head official" or "person who plays a major role."
2. As a noun meaning "the main portion of a financial account upon which interest is paid."
3. As an adjective meaning "main or primary."

Examples:

- The *principals* of the firm each purchased 1,000 shares of stock.
- We withdrew the interest—but not the *principal*—from our account.
- We believe that the *principal* reason for contamination at the site is the leaky underground storage tank.

### *Principle*

*Principle* is a noun that means "basic truth, belief, or theorem." Examples:

- He acted on his *principles* when he reported a fellow employee for overcharging a customer.
- The *principle* of free speech means the government allows people to speak even when it detests what they are saying.

■ Avogadro's *principle* states that if two equal volumes of gases are at the same temperature and pressure, they contain the same number of molecules.

## PRONOUN AGREEMENT AND REFERENCE

Pronouns—like *this, she, anyone,* and *they*—are words that substitute for nouns. The nouns to which pronouns refer are called "antecedents" of their respective pronouns. Pronouns provide a useful strategy for varying your style and avoiding needless repetition of nouns. However, their use requires vigilance in avoiding errors in agreement and reference. Here are the main rules:

### Make Pronouns Agree with Antecedents

Check every pronoun to make certain it agrees with its antecedent in number. That is, both noun and pronoun must be singular, or both must be plural. Of special concern are the pronouns *it* and *they*. Examples:

■ Norax, Inc., will complete *its* [not *their*] Argentina project next month.
■ The committee released *its* [not *their*] recommendations to all departments.

### Be Clear about the Antecedent of Every Pronoun

Leave no doubt about what noun a pronoun replaces. Any confusion about the antecedent of a pronoun can change the entire meaning of a sentence. To avoid such reference problems, rewrite a sentence or even repeat a noun rather than use a pronoun. Do whatever is necessary to prevent misunderstanding by your reader.

**Original:** The gas filters for these tanks are so dirty that they should not be used.

**Revision:** These filters are so dirty that they should not be used.

### Follow This *with a Noun*

A common stylistic error is the vague use of *this* as a pronoun, especially as the subject of a sentence. Sometimes the reference is totally confusing; sometimes it may be clear after several readings; and sometimes it is fairly clear but still a sign of a vague writing style. Using *this* as a pronoun often makes readers want to ask, "This what?" Make the subject of your sentence concrete, either by adding a noun after the *this* or by recasting the sentence.

**Original:** He talked every day about his upcoming trip to Europe. This irritated his colleagues.

**Revision:** He talked every day about his upcoming trip to Europe. This chatter irritated his colleagues.

OR

His constant talk about his upcoming European vacation irritated his colleagues.

## QUOTATION MARKS

In technical writing, you can use quotation marks for three main reasons:

1. To draw attention to particular words
2. To indicate passages taken directly from another source
3. To enclose titles of short documents such as reports or book chapters

As for punctuation, periods and commas go inside quotation marks. Semicolons and colons go outside of quotation marks. Examples:

- His presentation included the term "fuzzy logic"; however, he spent only a minute on the topic.
- In the section called "Closing," he included the following sentence: "Plant 624 will reopen next year."
- He mentioned the following criteria in his section entitled "Rationale": costs, productivity, and quality.

## REGRETTABLY/REGRETFULLY

*Regrettably* means "unfortunately," whereas *regretfully* means "with regret." When you are unsure of which word to use, substitute the above definitions to determine correct usage. Examples:

- *Regrettably,* the team members omitted their résumés from the proposal.
- François submitted his résumé to the investment firm, but, *regrettably,* he forgot to include a cover letter.
- I *regretfully* climbed on the plane to return home from Hawaii.

## *RESPECTIVELY*

Some good writers may use *respectively* to connect sets of related information. Yet such usage creates extra work for readers by making them reread previous passages. It is best to avoid *respectively* by rewriting the sentence, as shown in the several following options. Examples:

**Original:** Appendices A, G, H, and R contain the topographical maps for Sites 6, 7, 8, and 10, respectively.

**Revision—Option 1:** Appendix A contains the topographical map for Site 6; Appendix G contains the map for Site 7; Appendix H contains the map for Site 8; and Appendix R contains the map for Site 10.

**Revision—Option 2:** Appendix A contains the topographical map for Site 6; Appendix G for Site 7; Appendix H for Site 8; and Appendix R for Site 10.

**Revision—Option 3:** Topographical maps are contained in the appendices, as shown in the following list:

| *Appendix* | *Site* |
|------------|--------|
| A          | 6      |
| G          | 7      |
| H          | 8      |
| R          | 10     |

## *SEMICOLONS*

Consider the semicolon to be a modified period. It is frequently used as a less abrupt connector than a period. Example:

Five engineers left the convention hotel after dinner; only two returned by midnight.

One of the most common punctuation errors is the comma splice. It occurs when a comma instead of a semicolon or period is used in compound sentences connected by words like *however, therefore, thus,* and *then.* When these connectors separate two main clauses, either use a semicolon or start a new sentence. Example:

We made it to the project site by the agreed-upon time; however, [or, "time. However,"] the rain forced us to stay in our trucks for two hours.

As noted in the "Lists: Punctuation" entry on page 189, there is another instance in which you might use semicolons. Place them after the items in a list when you are treating the list like a sentence and when any one of the items contains internal commas.

## SENTENCE STRUCTURE: TERMINOLOGY

All writers have their own approach to sentence style. Yet every one of us has the same tools with which to work: words, phrases, clauses, and different sentence patterns. This entry defines some basic terms. The next one includes specific guidelines for organizing information in sentences. See the Parts of Speech entry for a complete description of terms for words. Only the most important ones—subjects and verbs—are discussed below.

### Subjects and Verbs

The most important parts of the sentence are the subject and the verb:

- *Subject:* names the person doing the action or the thing being discussed (*He* completed the study. / The *figure* contains his data).
- *Verb:* conveys action or state of being (She *visited* the site. / He *was* the manager).

### Phrases and Clauses

Words can be grouped into two main units, phrases and clauses:

- *Phrase:* lacks either a subject or a verb and thus must always relate to or modify another part of the sentence (She went *to the office. As project manager,* he had to write the report).
- *Clause:* has both a subject and a verb. It may stand by itself as a *main clause* and thus can be a complete sentence *(He talked to the group).* Or it may rely on another part of the sentence for its meaning and thus is a *dependent clause (After he left the site,* he went home).

### Sentence Types

There are four main types of sentences:

- *Simple:* contains one main clause *(He completed his work).*
- *Compound:* includes two or more main clauses connected by conjunctions *(Joe completed his work, but Mary stayed at the office to begin another job).*
- *Complex:* includes one main clause and at least one dependent clause *(After he finished the project, Jamal headed for home).*

■ *Compound-complex:* contains at least two main clauses and at least one dependent clause *(After they studied the maps, they left the project site, but they were unable to travel much farther that night)*.

---

## SENTENCE STRUCTURE: GUIDELINES

How you write and arrange sentences is largely a matter of personal writing style. Yet there are a few fundamental guidelines for all good business and technical writing:

### Place the Main Point Near the Beginning

One way to satisfy this criterion for good sentence style is to avoid excessive use of the passive voice (see the Active and Passive Voice entry). Another way is to avoid lengthy introductory phrases or clauses at the beginnings of sentences. The reader usually wants the most important information first.

> **Original:** After discussing the report submitted by the engineering consultant, it was decided by the committee to open a new office.

> **Revision:** The committee decided to open a new office after discussing the consultant's report.

### Focus on One Main Clause in Each Sentence

When you start stringing together too many clauses with *and* or *but,* you dilute the meaning of your text. An occasional compound or compound-complex sentence is acceptable, just for variety, but most sentences should be simple or complex.

### Vary Sentence Length, but Average No More than 15–20 Words

Place important points in short, emphatic sentences. Reserve longer sentences for qualifications and support of your main points. If you find your sentences run too long, there is a simple technique for shortening them. First find some long compound sentences connected by conjunctions like *and, but,* or *so.* Then separate them into shorter sentences by breaking them at the conjunction. Another strategy is to break sentences into two by separating the main point being made from supporting information.

> **Original:** Last week the human resources staff announced that the company is offering three new health plans because employees have

complained about the cost of the previous plans and the poor service provided.

**Revision:** Last week the human resources staff announced that the company is offering three new health plans. The change came about because of the cost and poor service of previous plans.

## *SET/SIT*

Like *lie* and *lay*, these two verbs are distinguished by form and use. Here are the basic differences:

1.  *Set* means "to place in a particular spot" or "to adjust." It is a transitive verb and thus takes a direct object to which it conveys action. Its main parts are *set* (present), *set* (past tense), *set* (past participle), and *setting* (present participle).
2.  *Sit* means "to be seated." It is usually an intransitive verb and thus does not take a direct object. Its main parts are *sit* (present), *sat* (past), *sat* (past participle), and *sitting* (present participle). It can be transitive when used casually as a direction to be seated. ("Sit yourself down and take a break.")

Examples:

- He *set* the computer on the table yesterday.
- While *setting* the computer on the table, he sprained his back.
- The technician had *set* the thermostat at 20 degrees.
- She plans to *sit* exactly where she sat last year.
- While *sitting* at her desk, she saw the computer.

## *SEXIST LANGUAGE: AVOIDING IT*

Language usually *follows* changes in culture, rather than *anticipating* such changes. A case in point is today's shift away from sexist language in business and technical writing—indeed, in all writing and speaking. The change reflects the increasing number of women entering previously male-dominated professions such as engineering, management, medicine, and law.

This section defines sexist and nonsexist language and suggests ways to avoid using gender-specific language in your writing.

### *Background on Sexism and Language*

Sexist language is the use of wording, especially pronouns like *he* or *him*, to represent positions or individuals who could be either men or women. For many years, it was common to use *he, his, him,* or other male words in sentences such as those that follow.

Examples of poor usage:

■ The operations specialist should check page 5 of his manual before flipping the switch.
■ Every physician was asked to renew his membership in the medical association before next month.
■ Each new student at the military academy was asked to leave his personal possessions in the front hallway of the administrative building.

These examples of obsolete usage assume that male pronouns and adjectives can stand for any persons—male or female. There are two good reasons to avoid such usage:

1.  The entry of many more women into the professions has called attention to the exclusionary nature of using male pronouns for indefinite use. Many readers will be bothered by such writing.
2.  The use of male pronouns in an indefinite context can be viewed as one way women are constrained from achieving equal status in the professions and, generally, in the culture. That is, such use of male pronouns fosters sexism in the society as a whole.

If you fail to rid your writing of sexist language, you risk drawing more attention to your style than to your ideas. Common sense argues for following some basic style rules to avoid sexist language.

## Guidelines for Nonsexist Language

This section offers techniques to help you shift from sexist to nonsexist language. Some of these strategies may not suit your taste in writing style; choose the ones that work for you.

### Avoid Personal Pronouns Altogether

An easy way to avoid problems with sexist language is to delete unnecessary pronouns from your writing.

**Sexist Language:** During his first day on the job, any new employee in the toxic-waste laboratory must report to the company doctor for his employment physical.

**Nonsexist Language:** During the first day on the job, each new employee in the toxic-waste laboratory must report to the company doctor for a physical.

## Use Plural Pronouns instead of Singular

Often you can shift from singular to plural pronouns without changing meaning.

> **Sexist Language:** Each geologist should submit his time sheet by noon on the Thursday before cheques are issued.

> **Nonsexist Language:** All geologists should submit their time sheets on the Thursday before cheques are issued.

Note also that you may encounter sexist language that inappropriately uses female pronouns in a generic manner. Such usage is just as flawed as male-oriented language.

> **Sexist Language:** Each nurse should make every effort to complete her rounds each hour.

> **Nonsexist Language:** Nurses should make every effort to complete their rounds each hour.

## Alternate Masculine and Feminine Pronouns

You can avoid sexist use by alternating *he* and *him* with *she* and *her*. However, do not switch pronoun use within too brief a passage, such as a paragraph or page. Instead, change every few pages, or every section or chapter. The drawback of this technique is that the alternating use of masculine and feminine pronouns tends to draw attention to itself. Also, the writer must work hard to balance the use of masculine and feminine pronouns, in a sense to give "equal treatment."

## Use Forms like *He or She*

This technique requires the writer to include both genders of pronouns each time indefinite use is required.

> **Sexist Language:** The president made it clear that each branch manager will be responsible for the balance sheet of his respective office.

> **Nonsexist Language:** The president made it clear that each branch manager will be responsible for the balance sheet of his or her respective office.

However, it is important to note that this style is bothersome to many writers who feel that *his or her* is wordy and awkward. Many readers are bothered even more by the forms *he/she, his/her,* and *him/her.*

## Shift to Second-Person Pronouns

Change to *you* and *your,* which are words without any sexual bias. For this technique to be effective, you need to be writing documents in which it is appropriate to use an instructions-related "command" tone associated with the use of *you*.

**Sexist Language:** After selecting her insurance option in the benefit plan, each new nurse should submit her paperwork to the Human Resources Department.

**Nonsexist Language:** Submit your paperwork to the Human Resources Department after selecting your insurance option in the benefit plan.

### Be Especially Careful of Titles and Letter Salutations

When you do not know how a particular woman prefers to be addressed, always use *Ms.* Even better, call the person's employer to ask whether *Miss, Mrs., Ms.,* or some other title is appropriate. (When calling, also check on the correct spelling of the person's name and her current job title.) When you do not know who will read your letter, never use *Dear Sir* or *Gentlemen* as a generic greeting. *Dear Sir or Madam* is also inappropriate. Instead, call the organization and get the name of a particular person to whom you can direct your letter. If you must write to a group of people, replace the generic greeting with an "attention" line that denotes the name of the group.

**Sexist Language:** Dear Sir: [to a collective audience]

**Nonsexist Language:** Attention: Admissions Committee

**Sexist Language:** Dear Miss Finnigan: [to a single woman for whom you can determine no title preference]

**Nonsexist Language:** Dear Ms. Finnigan:

# *SIC*

Latin for *thus*, this word is most often used when a quoted passage contains an error or other point that might be questioned by the reader. Inserted within brackets, *sic* indicates that the word or phrase before the *sic* was included in the original passage—and that it was not introduced by you. In other words, *sic* should be included when it is important that the reader be presented with a technically accurate quotation. Examples:

- The customer's letter to our Sales Department claimed that "there are too [*sic*] or three main flaws in the product."
- The proposal we received includes the following statement: "Work on each project will be overseen by a principle [*sic*] of the firm."

## SPELLING

All writers have words they find difficult to spell, and some writers have major spelling problems. Spell-checking software can help solve the problem. Yet you still must remain vigilant during the proofreading stage. Misspelled words in an otherwise well-written document cause readers to question the quality of the document and the professionalism of the writer.

This entry includes a list of commonly misspelled words. However, you should keep your own list of words you often have trouble spelling. Most of us have a relatively short list of words that give us repeated difficulty.

| | |
|---|---|
| absence | accumulate |
| accessible | accustomed |
| accommodate | achievement |
| acknowledgment | disappear |
| acquaintance | disappoint |
| admittance | disaster |
| advisable | disastrous |
| aisle | efficient |
| allotting | eligible |
| analysis | embarrass |
| analyze | endurance |
| Arctic | environment |
| athlete | equipment |
| athletic | equipped |
| awful | essential |
| basically | exaggerate |
| believable | existence |
| benefited | experience |
| bulletin | familiar |
| calendar | favourite |
| career | February |
| changeable | foreign |
| channel | foresee |
| column | forfeit |

commitment

committee

compatible

compelled

conscience

conscientious

conscious

controlled

convenient

definitely

dependable

descend

dilemma

ingenious

initially

initiative

insistence

interfered

interference

interrupt

irrelevant

judgment

knowledge

later

latter

liable

liaison

library

lightning

likely

loneliness

maintenance

manageable

manoeuvre

forty

fourth

genius

government

guarantee

guidance

handicapped

harass

height

illogical

incidentally

independence

indispensable

occurrence

omission

pamphlet

parallel

pastime

peculiar

possess

practically

preference

preferred

privilege

profession

professor

pronunciation

publicly

quantity

questionnaire

recession

reference

safety

similar

| | |
|---|---|
| mathematics | sincerely |
| medieval | specifically |
| mileage | subtle |
| miscellaneous | temperament |
| misspelled | temperature |
| mortgage | thorough |
| movable | tolerance |
| necessary | transferred |
| noticeable | truly |
| nuisance | undoubtedly |
| numerous | unmistakably |
| occasionally | until |
| occurred | useful |
| usually | wholly |
| valuable | writing |
| various | written |
| vehicle | |

## STATIONARY/STATIONERY

*Stationary* means "fixed" or "unchanging," whereas *stationery* refers to paper and envelopes used in writing or typing letters. Examples:

- To perform the test correctly, one of the workers had to remain *stationary* while the other one moved around the job site.
- When she began her own business, Julie purchased *stationery* with her new logo on each envelope and piece of paper.

## SUBJECT–VERB AGREEMENT

Subject–verb agreement errors are common in technical writing. They occur when writers fail to make the subject of a clause agree in number with the verb. ("The company president, along with his wife, are attending the meeting.") The verb *are* is not correct. The subject is *president*, so the verb should be *is*.

If you have agreement problems in your own writing, you can solve them by (1) isolating the subjects and verbs of all clauses in the document and (2) making certain that they agree. The main subject–verb agreement rules follow:

## Subjects Connected by **and** *Take Plural Verbs*

This rule applies to two or more words or phrases that, together, form one subject phrase. Example:

> The site preparation section and the foundation design portion of the report are to be written by the same person.

## Verbs after **Either/Or** *Agree with the Nearest Subject*

Subjects connected by *either/or* (or *neither/nor*) confuse many writers, but the rule is very clear. Your verb choice depends on the subject nearest the verb. Examples:

- He told his group that either the three reports or the proposal was to be completed this week.
- He told his group that either the proposal or the three reports were to be completed this week.

In the first example, the part of the subject closest to the verb is *proposal;* thus the correct verb form is *was*. In the second example, the part of the subject closest to the verb is *reports;* thus the correct verb form is *were*. Although both sentences are grammatically correct, the second is preferred because readers often view mixed *either/or* constructions as plurals. Singular verbs may sound awkward in such sentences.

## Verbs Agree with the Subject, Not with the Subjective Complement

Sometimes called a predicate noun or adjective, a subjective complement renames the subject and occurs after verbs like *is, are, was,* and *were*. Examples:

- The topic of the report is our high profits last year.
- Our high profits last year are the topic of the report.

## Prepositional Phrases Do Not Affect Matters of Agreement

*As long as, in addition to,* and *as well as* are prepositions, not conjunctions. A verb agrees with its subject, not with the object of a prepositional phrase. Example:

> The manager of human resources, as well as the technical managers, is supposed to meet with the three applicants.

## Collective Nouns Usually Take Singular Verbs

Collective nouns have singular form but usually refer to a group of persons or things (for example, *team, committee,* or *crew*). When a collective noun refers to a group as a whole, use a singular verb. Example:

The project crew was ready to complete the assignment.

Occasionally, a collective noun refers to the members of the group acting in their separate capacities. In this case, either use a plural verb or, to avoid awkwardness, reword the sentence. Examples:

- The crew were not in agreement about the survey locations. OR
- Members of the crew were not in agreement about the survey locations.

## Foreign Plurals Usually Take Plural Verbs

Although usage is gradually changing, most careful writers still use plural verbs with *data, strata, phenomena, media,* and other irregular plurals. Example:

The data he requested are incorporated into the three tables.

## Indefinite Pronouns like Each *and* Anyone Take Singular Verbs

Writers often fail to follow this rule when they make the verb agree with the object of a prepositional phrase instead of with the subject. Examples:

- Each of the committee members are ready to adjourn. (incorrect)
- Each of the committee members is ready to adjourn. (correct)

## THERE/THEIR/THEY'RE

These words can be easily misused by accident, even by those who know their correct use. Do a careful job of editing to make sure you have followed these guidelines:

1. Use *there* as an adverb that indicates direction or that is part of the phrases *there is* and *there are.*
2. Use *their* to indicate possession or ownership.
3. Use *they're* as a contraction for *they are.*

Examples:

- You'll find the new forms over *there* in the file cabinet.
- *There is* only one road to that village in Nepal.

- The secretaries and word processors were proud of *their* successful effort to rewrite the company's style manual.
- As for the board members, *they're* all planning to attend the reception tonight.

## TO/TOO/TWO

*To* is either part of the infinitive verb form ("to go") or a preposition in a prepositional phrase ("to the office"). *Too* is an adverb that either suggests an excessive amount or that conveys the meaning "also." *Two* is a noun or adjective that stands for the numeral 2. Examples:

- He volunteered *to* go [infinitive verb] *to* Yellowknife [prepositional phrase] *to* work [another infinitive verb form] on the project.
- Monika explained that the proposed hazardous waste dump would pose *too* many risks to the water supply. Scott made this point *too*.
- When *two* water mains broke, the city experienced a crisis.

## UTILIZE/USE

*Utilize* is simply a long form for the preferred verb *use*. Although some verbs that end in -*ize* are useful words, most are simply wordy substitutes for shorter forms. As some writing teachers say, "Why use *utilize* when you can use *use*?" Examples:

- She *used* [not *utilized*] the Internet for her research.
- Three different drills were *used* [not *utilized*] to drill through the rock.

## WHICH/THAT

*Which* is used to introduce nonrestrictive clauses, which are defined as clauses not essential to meaning (as in this sentence). Note that such clauses require a comma before the *which* and a slight pause in speech. *That* is used to introduce restrictive clauses that are essential to the meaning of the sentence (as in this sentence). Note that such clauses have no comma before the *that* and are read without a pause. *Which* and *that* can produce different meanings, as the following examples show:

- Our benefits package, *which* is the best in our industry, includes several options for dental care.
- The benefits package *that* our firm provides includes several options for dental care.
- My daughter's school, *which* is in York Region, has an excellent math program.
- The school *that* my daughter attends is in York Region and has an excellent math program.

Note that the above examples with *that* might be considered wordy by some readers. Indeed, such sentences often can be made more concise by deleting the *that* introducing the restrictive clause. However, delete *that* only if you can do so without creating an awkward, choppy sentence.

## WHO/WHOM

*Who* is a subjective form that can only be used as the subject of a clause; *whom* is an objective form that can only be used as a direct object or other non-subject noun form of a sentence. Examples:

- The man *who* you said called me yesterday is a good customer of the firm. [The clause "who . . . called me yesterday" modifies *man*. Within this clause, *who* is the subject of the verb *called*. Note that the subject role of *who* is not affected by the two words "you said," which interrupt the clause.]
- They could not remember the name of the person *whom* they interviewed. [The clause "whom they interviewed" modifies *person*. Within this clause, *whom* is the direct object of the verb *interviewed*. Grammatically, the clause could be turned around to read "they interviewed whom."]

## WHO'S/WHOSE

*Who's* is a contraction that replaces *who is*, whereas *whose* is a possessive adjective. Examples:

- *Who's* planning to attend the annual meeting?
- Susan is the manager *who's* responsible for training.
- *Whose* budget includes training?
- Susan is the manager *whose* budget includes training.

# WORDINESS

Some experts believe that careful attention to conciseness would shorten technical documents considerably—perhaps as much as 40 to 50 percent. As a result, reports and proposals would take less time to read and cost less to produce. This entry offers several techniques for reducing verbiage without changing meaning.

## *Replace Abstract Nouns with Verbs*

Concise writing depends more on verbs than it does on nouns. Sentences that contain abstract nouns, especially ones with more than two syllables, can be shortened by focusing on strong verbs. By converting an abstract noun to an action verb, you can eliminate extra words in each wordy sentence below:

> **Original:** The *acquisition* of the property was accomplished through long and hard negotiations.
>
> **Revision:** The property was *acquired* through long and hard negotiations.
>
> **Original:** *Confirmation* of the contract occurred yesterday.
>
> **Revision:** The contract was *confirmed* yesterday.
>
> **Original:** *Exploration* of the region had to be effected before the end of the year.
>
> **Revision:** The region had to be *explored* before the end of the year.
>
> **Original:** *Replacement* of the transmission was achieved only three hours before the race.
>
> **Revision:** The transmission was *replaced* only three hours before the race.

You can see that abstract nouns often end with *-tion* or *-ment*. Although such words are not always "bad" usage, they do cause problems when they replace the action verbs from which they are derived. In the following examples, abstract nouns are listed in the left column and the preferred verb forms are listed in the right column:

assessment          assess

classification      classify

computation         compute

delegation          delegate

| | |
|---|---|
| development | develop |
| disbursement | disburse |
| documentation | document |
| elimination | eliminate |
| establishment | establish |
| negotiation | negotiate |
| observation | observe |
| requirement | require |
| verification | verify |

## Shorten Wordy Phrases

Many wordy phrases have worked their way into business and technical writing. Such weighty expressions add extra words and rob prose of clarity. Here are some of the culprits, along with their concise substitutes:

| | |
|---|---|
| afford an opportunity to | permit |
| along the lines of | like |
| an additional | another |
| at a later date | later |
| at this point in time | now |
| by means of | by |
| come to an end | end |
| due to the fact that | because |
| during the course of | during |
| for the purpose of | for |
| give consideration to | consider |
| in advance of | before |
| in the amount of | for |
| in the event that | if |
| in the final analysis | finally |
| in the proximity of | near |
| prior to | before |
| subsequent to | later |
| with regard to | about |

## Replace Long Words with Short Ones

In school, most students rightly are taught to experiment with more sophisticated words. Although this effort helps build vocabularies, it also can encourage the lifelong tendency to use long words when short ones will do. As a rule, the following long words in the left column should be replaced by the short words in the right column:

| | |
|---|---|
| advantageous | helpful |
| alleviate | lessen, lighten |
| approximately | about |
| cognizant | aware |
| commence | start, begin |
| demonstrate | show |
| discontinue | end, stop |
| endeavour | try |
| finalize | end, complete |
| implement | do, carry out |
| initiate | start, begin |
| inquire | ask |
| modification | change |
| prioritize | rank, rate |
| procure | buy |
| terminate | end, fire |
| transport | move |
| undertake | try, attempt |
| utilize | use |

## Leave Out Clichés

Clichés are worn-out expressions that add extra words to your writing. Although they once were fresh phrases, they became clichés when they no longer conveyed their original meaning. You can make writing more concise by replacing them with a good adjective or two. Here are some clichés to avoid:

as plain as day

ballpark figure

efficient and effective

few and far between
last but not least
leaps and bounds
needless to say
reinvent the wheel
skyrocketing costs
step in the right direction

## Write like You Talk

Much wordiness results from talking around the topic. Sometimes called *circumlocution*, this flaw arises from a tendency to write indirectly. It can be avoided by reading passages aloud. Almost invariably, the sound of the words will make problems of wordiness quite apparent. Ask yourself, "How would I say this if I were talking to the reader in person?" Asking this question helps condense all kinds of inflated language. However, remember that even direct writing must retain a tactful, diplomatic tone when it contains negative or sensitive information.

> **Original:** We would like to suggest that you consider directing your attention toward completing the project before the commencement of the seasonal monsoon rains in the region of the project area.
>
> **Revision:** We suggest you complete the project before the monsoons begin.
>
> **Original:** At the close of the last phase of the project, a bill for your services should be expedited to our central office for payment.
>
> **Revision:** After the project ends, please send your bill immediately to our central office.
>
> **Original:** It is possible that the well-water samples collected during our investigation of the well on the site of the subdivision could possibly contain some chemicals in concentrations higher than is allowable according to the state laws now in effect.
>
> **Revision:** Our samples from the subdivision's well might contain chemical concentrations beyond that permitted by the state.

## Avoid There Are, It Is, *and Similar Constructions*

*There are* and *it is* are not good substitutes for concrete subjects and action verbs. Such constructions delay the delivery of information about who or what is doing something. They tend to make your writing lifeless and abstract. Avoid them by creating (1) main subjects that are concrete nouns and

(2) main verbs that are action words. The revised passages below give readers a clear idea of "who is doing what" in the subject and verb positions.

**Original:** There are many M&K projects that could be considered for design awards.

**Revision:** Many M&K projects could be considered for design awards.

**Original:** It is clear to the hiring committee that writing skills are an important criterion for every technical position.

**Revision:** The hiring committee believes that writing skills are an important criterion for every technical position.

**Original:** There were seven people who attended the meeting at the client's office in Fredericton.

**Revision:** Seven people attended the meeting at the client's office in Fredericton.

## Cut Out Extra Words

Delete extra words or redundant phrasing in your work. Sometimes the problem comes in the form of needless connecting words, like *to be* or *that*. Other times it shows itself as points made earlier that do not need repeating. Delete extra words when their use (1) does not add a necessary transition or (2) does not provide new information. (One important exception is the intentional repetition of main points for emphasis, as in repeating important conclusions in different parts of a report.) The examples below display a variety of examples of wordy writing, with corrections made in longhand:

- Preparing the client's final bill involves ~~the~~ checking ~~of~~ all *project* invoices ~~for the project.~~
- The report examined what the ABC project manager considered ~~to be~~ a technically acceptable risk.
- During ~~the course of~~ its field work, the ABC team will ~~be engaged in the process of~~ reviewing all ~~of the~~ notes ~~that have been~~ accumulated in previous studies.
- ~~Because of his position~~ as head of ~~the~~ ABC public relations group, ~~at ABC,~~ he planned ~~such that he would be able~~ to attend the meeting.
- She believed ~~that the~~ recruiting ~~of~~ more minorities for the technical staff is essential.
- The department must determine its ~~aims and~~ goals so that they can be included in ~~the~~ *ABC's 2002* annual strategic plan. ~~produced by ABC for the year of 2002.~~
- Most ABC managers ~~generally~~ agree that all ~~of the~~ company~~'s~~ employees ~~at all of the offices~~ deserve ~~at least~~ some ~~degree of~~ training each year ~~that they work for the firm.~~

## WORDS THAT AREN'T

Many non-words have worked their way into informal and formal usage. Listed below are some common examples.

| *Don't Use* | *Use* |
|---|---|
| alot | a lot |
| anyways | anyway |
| anywheres | anywhere |
| complected | complexioned |
| could of | could have |
| different than | different from |
| enthused | enthusiastic |
| hisself | himself |
| in regards to | regarding *or* about |
| irregardless | regardless |
| refer back to | refer to |
| repeat again | repeat |
| somewheres | somewhere |
| theirselves | themselves |
| use to *or* suppose to | used to *or* supposed to |
| would of | would have |

## YOUR/YOU'RE

*Your* is an adjective that shows ownership, whereas *you're* is a contraction for *you are*. Examples:

- *Your* office will be remodelled next week.
- *You're* responsible for giving performance appraisals.

# Index